WHITE TEACHER
IN A BLACK SCHOOL

WHITE TEACHER IN A BLACK SCHOOL

ROBERT KENDALL

THE DEVIN-ADAIR COMPANY
NEW YORK

Canadian Agents: Abelard-Schuman, Toronto
Library of Congress Catalog card number: 64-23748
Manufactured in the United States of America by H. Wolff, N. Y.

ACKNOWLEDGMENT

This work is dedicated to my cousin, the late Tom T. Chamales, for giving me the inspiration to write and to Lowney Handy whose encouragement made me begin.

My thanks to Gloria for all her patience and untiring assistance.

For their individual contributions I thank the following: Frances E. Leslie, Valah Kratt, Guy Tedesco, Ellen Peterson, William Schoun, Nancy Adams and my parents Mr. and Mrs. William A. Kendall.

AUTHOR'S NOTE

The original title of this book was *Never Say Nigger!*—until so much pressure against it began to be felt that the publisher and I felt it necessary to make the change. Salesmen, booksellers and even the jacket designer in hushed tones stressed their horror. Four-letter obscenities, it seems are all right these days, but not this one forbidden word. All the objections, let it be understood, came from whites. Almost all of the Negroes I interviewed found the title acceptable.

The book is based on my two years of actual teaching experience in two majority-Negro schools in Los Angeles, California.

In reading the book one might get the impression that

special schools are being depicted. Such is definitely not the case. I am writing about students attending regular everyday public schools in Los Angeles. In this city there are special correctional schools to handle severe disciplinary cases. In some of these the teachers are first trained as policemen.

All of the happenings in the book are based on actual truth with the following partially fictional exceptions: disposition of the race-prejudice charge at a home-and-school meeting, although the outcome is based on an actual incident; a student taking Chain Gang initiation rites, although the incident upon which the scene is based is factual; Lieutenant Swartz's involvement in certain incidents that are based on fact.

Certain character composites are necessitated by combining two years into one. None of the names in the book is the name of any actual person living or dead. Any resemblance of a name to an actual person's name is accidental.

R. K.

PREFACE

More than one hundred years ago, in speaking of America, British historian Lord Macauley warned, "Your republic will be as fearfully plundered and laid waste by barbarians in the Twentieth Century as the Roman Empire was in the Fifth, with this difference; that the Huns and Vandals who ravaged the Roman Empire came from without and your Huns and Vandals will have been engendered within your own country, by your own institutions."

WHITE TEACHER IN A BLACK SCHOOL

1

"You don't call my mother no whore and get by with it, you dirty sonofabitch!"

I jerked around as one boy jackknifed another boy to the floor and began pounding him viciously with his fists. I raced back down the hall where students were running up from all directions. Pushing my way through them, I got to the boys who were slugging it out on the floor and pulled the bigger one off the smaller one. Beads of sweat poured down his lean black face and onto his torn shirt. His angry eyes looked at me as if he were prepared to lunge.

"What's your name?" I asked.

"What's yours?" A nasty sneer crossed his lips.

One of the other students yelled, "That's Billy Parrish!"

Billy blurted, "You simple-minded fink! I'll get you!"

I turned to the smaller boy who had now risen from the floor. "What's your name?"

A broad grin widened his round, dark face. "I'm Roger Gates," he said, "and I was just telling the truth. Everybody knows that Billy Parrish's old lady is a whore!"

The surrounding kids burst into wild laughter. I held Billy back as he lunged for Roger. "That's enough, from both of you!" I said.

A big, burly boy with a wide-open face shouldered his way through the crowd. "I'm the class president, Teach," he said. "You want me to take these two studs down to the cooler?"

"The cooler?"

"The Vice-Principal's office," he explained. "The cooler."

"What's your name?"

"George Washington."

I nodded. "Okay, George. Tell him that Mr. Brent caught them fighting in the hall." I turned to Billy and Roger. "You can tell the Vice-Principal your story."

Billy made a mocking bow. "Yes, *sir.*"

"Come on, get goin', you studs!" George Washington roughly pushed the boys through the crowd and down the hall.

I went on to my homeroom, unlocked the door,

and stood back while the homeroom boys stampeded into the room. I then went to my desk where I stood observing the noisy confusion. It was the first schoolday of the year. It was my first day, officially, as a schoolteacher, although I'd had one practice year. This particular school, in downtown Los Angeles, was ninety percent Negro. And I was a white man.

The opening bell rang and I ordered the boys to take seats. Pushing, scrambling, and arguing loudly, they all finally sat down. But the loud laughter, talking and arguing continued. "Quiet!" I tried to out-voice them. "I want quiet in here at once!"

The noise sizzled down. The bugle sounded for the flag salute. A few of the boys ambled to their feet but most of them ignored the call. I slapped the ruler on the desk with angry insistence. There was a slow, hostile, but final respect paid to the flag.

"All right," I said when it was over, "sit down."

When they were all seated, I, too, sat down, and spoke gravely. "Boys, our flag stands for many things of great value to all of us. To the nation, generally, and to each and every one of us, individually. We must always show absolute respect for this flag. It is the symbol of our freedom, the sign which assures us that we live in a country founded on justice and equality for all—"

A raspberry, loud, clear, and unmistakable, came from the back of the room. The entire classroom exploded into raucous laughter.

At that moment the bell rang. Before I could make one small measure of discipline, they were all on their feet, stampeding out of the room.

In a moment, I was alone with the echo of their derisive laughter and the stampeding of their feet—and my own concern for the future. What had I done wrong? How had I got off to such a bad start?

Or was it *me,* personally? Could it possibly be just because I was a white teacher in a black school that I had failed to receive one small show of respect?

My Period One students began streaming in. When they were finally seated, I introduced myself, then said, "Now, since I'm new here, why don't we try to become acquainted, first of all . . ."

It was the last class of the day that completely arrested my attention. There was Captain Smith, a short, stout boy who actually crawled into the room on all fours. He crawled to the bookcase and got the Yellow Pages telephone directory. Then he crawled to a seat and happily began thumbing through the pages.

There was Billy Parrish, an obvious troublemaker, always picking fights, using filthy language, and showing no respect for authority at all. I would look up in class and find him staring at me with an expression as close to homicidal hatred as I could imagine.

There was no course in college that had prepared me for the impudence, sarcasm and defiance which I found to be the rule rather than the instance. More and more as the day progressed I became convinced that the defiance did not stem from the fact I was trying to teach them and control them but because I was white.

After the final class bell rang I told Captain Smith to put the Yellow Pages away and take out his text. He refused. When I tried to take the Yellow Pages away from him, he started sobbing wildly.

"You dirty rat!" he cried, "You live in a house with

bubblegum wrappers for wallpaper and you eat out of garbage cans!"

When I told a girl named Marion Blackwell to put her gum in the waste basket, she said with an ugly sneer, "You're race-prejudiced, aren't you, Mr. Brent?"

Near the end of the class, a tall, attractive girl, Angelina Childers, took out a compact and began applying lipstick to her already thickly crimsoned lips. I ordered her to put the things away.

"The hell I will!" she said loudly.

It was the final straw. "If you don't put those things away immediately," I said angrily, "I'll send you to the Principal's office!"

She laughed sharply. "Don't try to hand me that scare shit! You can't scare me!"

Amid the shrieks of laughter, I wrote a note explaining what had happened, then I sent Angelina, accompanied by a seemingly more reliable student, to the Principal's office. Shortly after that the school day happily came to an end. As I gathered my things together, I thought, *Well, Brent, there it is. Your first day as a teacher*. And some small being on my shoulder, angel or devil, seemed to whisper, *Are you sure you don't wish it were your last?*

When I checked in my box in the office, I found a note from Principal Towers saying he wanted to see me before I left. When I went to his private office, he asked me to sit down, and was very pleasant. He was a big hulk of a man with a bland face and a bristling, sandy crew cut. He leaned far back in his swivel chair and asked, "How did it go, Brent?"

I said, "Well, I had my troubles."

He nodded. "The first day is always the hardest." Then with a light chuckle, he said, "Remember when you were a kid? Well, kids today are just about the same. They use a lot of words we used to use. We just have to overlook it."

I frowned. "Are you talking about Angelina Childers?"

He nodded again and leaned heavily forward on his desk. "I'm a busy man, as most high school principals are. My time is taken up with committee meetings for everything you could imagine. For example, I have to meet with the Clean Grounds Committee in ten minutes. Tomorrow, it's the New Organ Project Committee. The day after that, the meeting of the departmental heads, and so on. . . ."

He paused for a show of understanding so I nodded.

"So you see, Mr. Brent, that if I took time out to take care of every kid in this school who used dirty words, I might *never* leave the office."

"I understand," I said evenly.

"Good."

I rose to go then decided to speak to him about Captain Smith who had greatly concerned me. "This boy doesn't belong in a regular classroom at all, Mr. Towers. He is obviously retarded and I can't imagine how he ever advanced to B9 English."

His massive head cocked slightly to one side. "You know the philosophy of progressive education and our social adjustment policies, don't you, Brent?"

"Well, I believe I do."

"Then you should know the answer to your own question. The word 'progress,' for example. Progress means some sort of advancement or improvement, doesn't it?"

I agreed.

"Well, Captain Smith has made some measure of improvement every year so he has been advanced every year."

"You mean, then, that there is *no* set standard of achievement for the subject matter from one grade to the next," I said.

His smile was somehow Buddhistic. "Well, yes . . . and no. That, I suppose, is the general philosophy."

I instinctively felt I was following a dangerous path but I went on. "Then a dog might graduate if he made any progress in learning, Mr. Towers. If he could retrieve a ball in A7, a bone in A8, and bark on cue in A9, he would have made progress and be eligible for a diploma."

"That would be progress, yes," he said tightly. "They do have dog training schools where they teach dogs and graduate them and give them degrees. What's your point?"

I had the same sense of insecurity which I'd felt all day but I managed to smile. "Well, I'm not quite sure, Mr. Towers. It just seems to me that if my job means passing children who can neither read nor write with any degree of skill—and Captain Smith is one of these—then I'm helping them get a diploma which in actuality, means nothing. And doesn't this mean that education means nothing? Because it does not truly exist?"

He laughed drily. "Brent, you're taking this thing

much too seriously. For your own good, take it easy. Just do the best you can and see to it that your kids all pass their grades. That's all."

I smiled. "For my own good, Mr. Towers?"

"For your own good, Mr. Brent," he smiled.

2

As I maneuvered my car onto the freeway and into the swiftly moving traffic, I couldn't help but think that my first day as a schoolteacher had not been what one might call a howling success. It had begun with a fight and ended with a threat—with a small personal hell lying in between.

I wondered what I would tell my sister when she called to find out how things had gone. Helen had been adamantly against my taking an assignment in a ninety percent Negro school. Her first year's teaching assignment had also been in a majority Negro school, as are most beginners in metropolitan communities, due to the rapid turnover of teachers in the Negro areas. "You're making a big mistake, Bob," she'd told me. "Tell the Board you've changed your mind. Tell them you want to work in a school near where you live. Tell them *anything*—but don't let yourself be thrown into a hotbed of blacks!"

I had not followed her advice. She had warned, "You'll be sorry, believe me. There is no punishment which will strike either morality into their souls or intelligence into their minds. They're dead set on believing that if you're white, you're an enemy, and the few bright ones you get, who haven't been completely poisoned against you, aren't worth what you have to put up with from the others. It's just no use!"

Helen's one year at a Negro school had completely changed her attitude toward the Negroes. She had grown up with Negro friends and had never categorized anyone according to race. It had never been "they" or "them" with her but always "he" and "she." However, by the end of that first teaching year, she had admitted total defeat and defied any other white person to have either the fortitude or the genius to be successful teaching Negro children.

At the time, I had silently wondered if Helen's failure might not lie within herself. Because of her unique Grecian beauty, she had always been placed upon a pedestal. She had been one of those rare and fortunate beings whom life just naturally seems to spoil. Things were always, somehow, made easy for her. She graduated from the University with high scholastic honors, and had a score of "Queenships" to her credit. Because of such a background, had she been equipped to cope with children of a minority group, spawned recklessly in one of the most underprivileged and impoverished sections of the city? Were the Negro children themselves so impossible or had it been Helen's own shortcomings that had kept her from truly assuming the role of the teacher who must be dedicated solely to her students?

Whatever the answer was, she had given up teaching after that one year. She went back to the University, got her master's degree, and became a counsellor in a school where she had her own office, was back on a pedestal again, and was happy working with "decent white people."

As I drove off the freeway ramp toward the Los Feliz district, I thought of Mother. She was as prejudiced against the Negroes as Helen but it had come into being over a longer period of time and the motivation was much more tangible. She and Father had immigrated to a small midwestern town where they had worked hard and eventually been able to buy a large, two-story house in one of the old, fine sections. When Father died, Mother converted the house into twelve small, single units. They were attractively furnished and well kept, and within a short period of time, she had a waiting list of bachelors and career girls who wanted to rent from her.

As modern housing tracts began springing up in the suburbs, the older section of town became less desirable. People began selling their homes, many to Negroes. As the Negroes moved in, more white people moved out. The more white people moved out, the more Negroes moved in. It has happened everywhere, in all cities and most towns.

Through the years, Mother had been advised to sell but she'd always refused. "My most beloved memories live in this house," she'd maintained stubbornly, "and this is where I'll die."

Before long, Mother was the last white outpost in the area, or as she put it, "I'm a white island in a black sea." The waiting list was a thing of the past. She was lucky if half her units were rented, and because she could only get lower type tenants, luckier still if they didn't skip out without paying the rent.

At last, she thought seriously about selling but she had overstayed her time. The property had become virtually worthless.

As I pulled into the driveway of the large hillside home where I had a small apartment, I felt a familiar twinge of pain at Mother's predicament. She couldn't be blamed for wanting to protect the things she had earned through hard work.

Identity—that is what the Negro is really reaching for, I thought, an image that he can be proud of—and until the Negro achievement is strikingly significant he will flounder in a dismal sea of social discontent and social misconceptions. Education—that is the *only* answer, I thought. And as an educator I determined I would set high academic standards to help him find a positive identity in the future. I knew it wasn't going to be easy. But was there anything worthwhile that was easy?

I pulled into my driveway and, as I went to my apartment, the phone was ringing. It was my sister Helen. I told her, "It was rough but I liked the challenge!"

3

When I got to school the next morning I picked up the mimeographed daily bulletin. There was to be a faculty meeting at 3:05 in the library. "Punctuality, please!"

The Principal's secretary called out to me. "I'm terribly sorry, Mr. Brent, but I forgot to tell you yesterday that you are to bring the doughnuts for the faculty meeting. The new teachers get them for the older ones."

"Sure," I said. "I'll be glad to."

"There are seventy-five teachers and we should have at least two doughnuts each," she explained solemnly.

"You can get them at a little place around the corner. You can phone and they'll deliver."

"Okay, fine."

"Oh—the teachers like the different flavors," she added.

I wanted to laugh but I said, "If you'd be so kind as to phone for the flavors you think they'd like, I'll write you a check for whatever it is."

She added. "I can pay for them out of petty cash and you can reimburse me."

"Good." I went on to my homeroom. George Washington, who had taken the two young savage warriors to the so-called cooler the morning before, had turned out to be one of my homeroom boys. He was waiting for me, insisted on taking my briefcase for me, and we went into the room together. My herd of wild young bulls came stampeding in and my second day as a schoolteacher was off to a roaring start. But perhaps because of my own sense of rejuvenation, the kids didn't seem to be quite so noisy that morning. Maybe they'd gotten their second wind after the first day jitters, too, I thought hopefully.

When the lunch bell rang, I went to the cafeteria, purchased a tray of food, and sat down at the nearest table.

"Sorry, this table is taken," a young Negro teacher informed me.

I looked at her, surprised at her brittle tone. Her eyes met mine and I saw happy contempt flashing from them. I moved to another table but I still felt her penetrating gaze upon me. *What had I done now,* I wondered.

I had just cut my first bite of meat loaf when

a teacher bustled up to me, saying hurriedly, "You will have hall duty during the last fifteen minutes of your lunch period, Mr. Brent."

I looked up at her. "But my lunch period is only thirty minutes!"

"I know." She nodded peremptorily and hurried off.

I gulped my food and rushed to my post in the hall. The Boys' Vice-Principal was waiting. "Something detain you?" he asked, looking gravely at his watch.

"Just trying to finish lunch," I answered.

"We've got to watch these kids all the time, Brent," he warned.

"Yes, sir."

"We have a goof sheet," he went on ominously, "to help keep the teachers in shape, you understand. If a teacher goofs on any assignment, he receives a check on the goof sheet. The daily sheet goes to the Principal and he uses it in making his analysis of the teacher for the downtown board evaluation."

"I see," I said evenly. "I'll try to stay off the goof sheet."

"It's a good idea—for your own sake."

I watched him walk down the hall. It seemed that just about everything in this school was 'for my own sake.' I tried to recall some part-time college job I'd had which only allowed fifteen minutes for lunch. I couldn't.

After lunch, when I went to my classroom, I found still another surprise waiting for me. The blackboard was peppered with spit wads. The floor was littered with wads of paper. I could feel the students' eager eyes upon me. I stood for a moment, outwardly revealing no expression, inwardly controlling my anger, then without comment, I began picking up the papers. On one, I glimpsed a dirty picture some kid had drawn.

I threw the papers into the wastebasket and said firmly, "Okay, people, you're a long time out of kindergarten. Why don't you act like it? I want this place kept clean—no ifs, ands or buts!"

There were a couple of sniggers. Geraldine Robinson waved her hand and announced, "I got student government every Tuesday this period, Mr. Brent!"

Seven other students immediately repeated her words. They all rushed up to me and produced cards which read: *Students must be dismissed from any classes for Student Government meetings.* The cards were signed by Mr. Towers.

I let them go and tried quickly to reorganize my schedule. With so many of the class gone, I would have to skip homework. "All right, class, if you'll get out your paper and pencils."

The door opened. A student came in and handed me a sheet of paper. It read: "Select the homeroom boy you want to be your Boys' Club representative." It, too, was signed by Mr. Towers. Having only seen the boys in two homeroom periods, I knew I couldn't make a fair decision as yet, so I wrote a note back to the office saying I needed more time to decide.

Within ten minutes, the class was interrupted again with another note from Mr. Towers. "Please follow instructions, Brent. We have a 2:30 deadline for all homeroom teachers to have chosen representatives. Do not delay!" With disgust and anger I checked two names on my list of homeroom boys. I didn't even know the kids but meeting a deadline and satisfying the Principal seemed more important—"for my own sake."

At last, the three o'clock closing bell rang. I was supposed to be in the library punctually at five after three. However, the *Teacher's Manual* stated that the teacher must stand outside the classroom door for five minutes after the close of school at three. "That's easy," I thought, "All I have to do is be in two places at once."

I didn't laugh when I walked into the library at ten after three. The doughnuts and the rest of the faculty were there. Only I was late. I made a mental note to find out how they managed the miracle.

Library tables were pushed together and heaps of doughnuts were gathered around silver coffee pots. The teachers were drinking coffee, eating doughnuts, and joking among themselves. The Principal was standing at the front desk, smiling and washing down a pink-covered doughnut with coffee. I found a seat next to Miss Joseph, whose homeroom connected with mine, and sat down.

"Mr. Towers looks like a football player," I whispered, trying to make conversation.

"He was," she smiled. "The Los Angeles school board seems to believe it's a good policy to pick physical education majors for Principals."

"Why?" I asked in surprise.

She shrugged. "Don't ask me. Ask the Board of Education." She leaned closer and whispered sardonically, "It's a good idea to talk sports with him."

The Principal jangled a little bell and the teachers, who had been about as noisy as my homeroom boys, quieted down.

"Welcome back, faculty," he boomed jovially. "And welcome, newcomers. I hope you all had a good time this summer and are raring to go. I hear that Harry Waterfield, our Boys' Counselor had a bang-up vacation in France, could hardly tear himself away from the —er—country to come home!" He laughed heartily and the faculty followed suit. Then he continued. "Well, faculty, we're each and every one of us here for one purpose and one purpose only—payday!" More laughter. "Seriously, we're here to help these kids get an education. It's up to you to do everything in your power to see to it that each student passes the subject he's taking from you. Remember, when you flunk a student, you are in effect failing yourself!"

The place was quiet. The Progressive Educational dogma flowed on and on and on. My mind wandered. I asked myself, what is a school? A school is to stimulate the young mind and to educate the young mind. It is to motivate a better way of life. In this school, there were kids who hadn't had an easy lot. They were hostile toward each other, toward the world, and worst of all, toward themselves. True education was the only answer—

"We must particularly watch the kids on nutrition-breaks and during lunch period," Mr. Towers was saying. "And we're asking some of you nice teachers to stay for one hour after school and help keep the boys off the streets and on our athletic field. There is nothing better than a lot of sports activities. . . ."

And on and on. At last, there was enthusiastic applause and the meeting ended.

Mr. Towers motioned to me across the room.

I weaved to him through the milling teachers. "Yes, sir?"

He leaned forward and said softly, "Don't forget to pay for the doughnuts on your way out!"

4

When I woke up Saturday morning, I knew two things for sure. I was very tired and I was very glad it was Saturday. I had been going at such a highly accelerated pace all week, it was almost a weary letdown not having to race up and out.

I spent a leisurely week end and put off correcting papers until Sunday night. I was, as usual, shocked by the illiteracy of my students. I had asked them to write whether they thought our school was a courteous school. They answered: "No because there always choppin on each others mother and half of them don't even know each others mother." "Cuseing! Cuseing is bad and can get you into a lot of trouble and it is very un mannerly and selfush." "It is courteous in some ways but some of the kids in the school is just bad. But I will tell you one thing This Dump is better than some dumps cause it got much nicer things in it. We have more activityies." "I think it aint courteous. Because theres lots of kids who say bad words and they chop on each other." "They go around thinking there big. Som of them get into frights." "I can not say yes or no because I haven' been here long enuf in this sckol." "Some of the kids in this dump walk by you, knox you books out of your hands and won't bother to pick them up but some pupil do not act this way."

Correcting constant error is exhausting work. It was after one when I finally went to bed. I seemed to close my eyes and the alarm went off. I snapped on the light. It was six A.M.

I lay back a moment, almost wallowing in my weariness. But the picture of Mr. Towers standing at the sign-in sheet in the front office kept tugging at me. If we were one minute less than thirty minutes arriving before classes began, he considered us late and we got a check on his neat little goof sheet.

As I hurriedly dressed, I thought of Mr. Towers' smile when he'd ask, "What detained you, Brent?" It was that damned, condescending smile that got under my skin! He smiled when you were early and he smiled when you were late, and no matter which, his smile looked as if it had been frozen in ice.

Outside, the smog was as thick and dark as my spirits. On the freeway, traffic snarled, as it always did in such smog conditions. Headlights were turned on and cars were inching along, bumper to bumper. And sure enough, even though I'd left my place in plenty of time, when I signed in at school, I was five minutes late.

"What detained you, Brent?" Mr. Towers smiled—oh, yes, he smiled!

"Smog," I said flatly, and hurried to my homeroom, aware as I walked out of the office that he was putting a check next to my name on his goof sheet.

George Washington was waiting for me outside the door, as usual. "Morning, Mr. Brent," he said, full of vigor.

I recalled the Principal warning me about George after school on Friday. "George, I understand you socked Billy Parrish in the eye."

"Just a love tap, Mr. Brent," the boy grinned. "That's the only way to keep some of these studs in line."

"Well, easy on the love, kid," I smiled. "Mr. Towers doesn't approve of it."

I went into my homeroom and began putting some pictures up on the bulletin board. The bell rang and the homeroom boys herded in as George stood rigidly, arms folded, at the front of the room. The boys quieted down when Billy Parrish came in boasting a mean-looking shiner.

Billy walked up to George and stood glowering wrathfully up at him. George snarled, "Move on, Parrish! Ain't you learned your lesson yet?" Billy made an ugly coughing sound, as if he were going to spit. George held his doubled fist in the smaller boy's face. With a snort, Billy went to his seat.

The bell rang. We stood, said the pledge to the flag, and another day, another week had officially begun.

The days glided by. As I peered through the educator's kaleidoscope, the pattern of the students' conduct would change positions over and over. I surveyed them from ever-changing angles. It seemed that the patterns made little sense—meaningless designs of wrong conduct.

The last class of the day was my most dreaded class. Problem by problem they came in.

My problem was finding some way to reach them and help them want to do good work. But reaching them was no small problem in itself, because they didn't want to be reached. It was easier for them to wallow in a rut of "just getting by," with antagonism and resentment their sentinels guarding that rut.

Roger Gates came in and sat down. He took out a yoyo and began rolling it up and down as he whistled loudly.

"Put the yoyo away, Roger," I told him.

"Aw, Teach! Can't I have any fun?" he wailed.

"You heard me, Roger."

Marion Blackwell came in. As she passed my desk, she flashed me a contemptuous look. "Hello, Marion," I said. She went to her seat without answering.

Captain Smith crawled in on all fours. I decided to ignore him. He crawled across the room and back again. Then, getting no response from me, he jumped up, ran to my desk, and began pulling out the drawers.

"Close those drawers and get to your seat, Smith," I ordered.

He slammed the drawers shut. Then he jumped up on my chair and blew his foul breath in my face.

"Go to your seat," I said.

"You hate me," he yelled. "Well, I hate you! I hate all teachers but I hate you the most!"

I spotted two slips of paper in his shirt pocket. "Where did you get those hall passes?" I asked, reaching for them.

He jumped off the chair, screaming. "They're not yours! I stole them from the gym teacher and they're mine!"

I took the passes from him. He began crying, fell down to his hands and knees, and crawled over to the bookshelves. He got the Yellow Pages and crawled to his desk. He stuck his thumb in his mouth, and with soft, broken sobs began feverishly tearing through the pages.

The bell rang and the class quieted. Ruby Burns, a girl with a badly scarred face whom the kids cruelly called "Radiation," was reading a confession magazine.

"Put your magazine away, Ruby," I told her.

Her eyes narrowed hatefully. "Okay! Here's your dirty old magazine if you wanna read it so bad," she screamed, and threw the magazine at me as hard as she could.

I picked up the magazine, put it in a drawer of my desk, and began the lesson.

They had just started a writing assignment when the quiet was interrupted by Geraldine Robinson. "You cut that out, Billy," she shouted. "Some of us are trying to study!"

"What is it, Geraldine?" I asked.

"Billy Parrish keeps leanin' over his desk and puttin' his hands on my—"

"She's lyin'!" Billy yelled.

Geraldine jumped up, holding up her skirt. "I'm not

lyin'!" Her eyes were moist with emotion. "Look at his hand prints on my dress! He's got printer's ink from shop all over his hands and now I got to get my dress cleaned and I don't have no money!"

Billy laughed shrilly. "You know how to earn money, don't you, Geraldine? Ask your old man for some of that booze money you earn for him!"

Geraldine jerked around. "You dirty black nigger," she screamed hysterically, "I'll kill you! I'll kill you!"

Swiftly, I went down the aisle and pulled her away from Billy. "Come with me into the hall, Geraldine," I said.

She gave Billy a look of seething hatred and followed me. I stood at the door, trying to keep one eye on the class which had erupted into talk and laughter. Geraldine began crying softly.

"I'm sorry, Mr. Brent," she said. "But I hate that Billy Parrish. He's mean and nasty."

Geraldine, you must learn to control yourself," I told her. "You can't go through life getting so angry that you begin hitting people. That's no answer."

"Yes, Mr. Brent," she said quietly, her eyes still moist. "I know you're right."

"Will you try to control yourself?" I asked.

"I'll try, Mr. Brent," she said in a low voice.

"Good. You'd be surprised how much we can do just by trying."

We went back into the room. Angelina, the girl who wore skin-tight skirts and peasant blouses which should have come two inches higher on her bust, was giggling about something with Billy Parrish. Captain Smith was still engrossed in the Yellow Pages. Ophelia

Hernandez, the small, pale Mexican girl, was staring blankly out the window as usual. Ophelia never caused me any trouble. She never did any work, either. Roger Gates was playing with his yoyo.

I finally quieted the class and sent them back to work. As I went on correcting papers, I thought about Geraldine. She was a beautiful girl with smooth, chocolate-colored skin, and a soft, gentle look in her eyes. She spoke, as a rule, in a modulated voice. I couldn't help but wonder what the problem was that had put her under such emotional tension she seemed always on the verge of tears.

I decided to look into the files in the Counseling Department to see what I could find out about her, and about some of the others. Perhaps, if I knew their backgrounds better I'd discover what tactics to use in reaching them.

When the school day was over, I got the records I wanted and took them back to my homeroom. On each record was the child's name, his vital statistics, and comments from the different teachers who'd had him as a student.

I glanced over Captain Smith's file. "—a seriously retarded child. He has frequent emotional outbursts and often gets down on all fours and crawls around the room." This comment was initialed by a fourth grade teacher. The fifth grade teacher wrote, "Captain Smith is unable to write one good sentence and I doubt if he can read at all. It is very discouraging." The sixth grade teacher made no comment but the seventh grade teacher wrote, "I tried to visit Captain Smith's parents. His older brother had gotten into trouble with the law and his father told me he wasn't letting any strangers come in and talk to his boy unless they had a search warrant. I've sent many notes home asking for a consultation but have never received an answer of any kind."

Captain Smith had scored very low on every test he had taken.

I added my own footnote: "Captain Smith crawls into class to get attention and insists on reading the Yellow Pages constantly. When thwarted, he is inclined to have serious emotional outbursts. He seldom makes any effort at doing his work." I initialed the Cumulative Record card and thought, "impossible to educate" might have been the simplest and only necessary thing to write. This child certainly did not belong in English B9. Actually he didn't belong in a public school with normal children.

I went on to the next file. Of Angelina, her fifth grade homeroom teacher wrote, "I caught her in a lie. She tried to tell me that she saw another girl take the Homeroom Cookie Campaign money from my desk. However, when I caught her in my purse one day, I realized she was probably the thief." A sixth grade teacher wrote, "Angelina is a troublemaker. She seldom does her work and talks out in class any time she feels like it." Another teacher wrote, "Angelina is always egging the boys on by flirting with them and seems to enjoy the unwholesome advances they make toward her."

I glanced over Ruby Burns' file. "Ruby has trouble in all her classes because the children make fun of the scars on her face. They nicknamed her 'Radiation' because of these scars which she suffered in a fire when her mother and father were killed. She lives in a foster home."

Of Geraldine, it was written: ". . . basically a good, kind girl but lazy. She has no incentive to work." Another teacher wrote, "She always seems to be in a position of defending herself, and is given to uncontrolled bursts of temper. Broods a great deal but seldom given to discussing any personal problem."

Billy Parrish's file was the most disturbing of all. "Billy Parrish threw a chair at me and I ducked. The chair broke on my desk. I sent him to Social Adjustment but I doubt if that's going to do much good. The child has a violent nature and could be dangerous." Then I read, "Billy Parrish had a long razor which we discovered during weapons check." I was shocked at the idea a weapons check was necessary and wondered how often they were held. Then I read on: "When I brought in Billy's parents, they said they honestly did not know how to control him. They were from the deep south and seemed like nice people who wanted to help, but both admitted complete helplessness in trying to discipline Billy. This child should be carefully watched."

I looked at the folders on my desk. Just a few fleeting facts scribbled hastily by tired teachers about a few small human beings. They weren't really much help, I thought despondently. And yet, those folders held the different psychological pieces of the jigsaw puzzles which fitted into a giant mosaic of a blurred design. In that design was the students' troubled today, and a perilous prediction of their terrible tomorrow.

5

The days threaded into a design of my own personal mosaic. I was constantly on guard against the seeds of hatred ready to blossom at any moment from my students—hatred, first, for my color, next, for my position of authority.

There were so many meetings, so much to do, so many homework papers to correct every night, I found myself indulging in no form of recreation at all. I repeatedly turned down invitations from my sister to come over for Saturday night get-togethers or Sunday dinner, and excused myself from meeting friends. Week nights, I was too busy and week ends, I was too tired. Occasionally, I would take in a solitary movie matinee on Sunday, but beyond that I simply had no energy. My thoughts and energies were constantly going out to my students.

More than anything else, I was trying to get the concept of true education across. I thought that if they could be made to understand what it meant, they might try to achieve it. My thoughts were going along this line one morning as I was on my way to class. George Washington raced up to me, taking my case.

"How are you doing in all your school work?" I asked him.

"I'm coolin' it, man," he grinned.

"It's important for you to get good grades," I told him. "But more important is that you become genuinely interested in what you're doing. Interested enough to want to go beyond what the teacher assigns and do some work on your own."

"Are you kiddin', Teach?" he laughed.

"No, I'm not kidding, George. School should trigger your mind and make you want to get more knowledge on your own. What you want to learn will be of much more value to you than what you are simply forced to learn in order to pass."

"All I know, Teach, is that I want to get good grades so I can get me a diploma and get a good job and a snazzy car and a sassy chick!"

I smiled. "Well, I'm glad to know you've got a lot of plans. It's good to have goals in life. But if you just want to get a diploma with the idea it will mean money for a car and a girl, you've got the wrong idea of true education."

"Come again, man," he grinned. "You diggin' the trench way over my head."

I laughed as we went into the classroom. There was something likeable about Geroge, something clean and wholesome. Unlike so many of his fellow students whose minds were rancid with hostilities and who cringed away from any effort on my part to reach them, George was always eager to meet me halfway.

"The student who has true education, George," I explained, "is the one who doesn't work just for grades. First, he works for the information which will help him find out what he can do best in life. Then he works to learn how to do it in the very best way possible. A doctor wouldn't be much of a doctor if all he cared about was the money, would he?"

"No, I guess not," he said emphatically. Then he turned suddenly bashful, shuffling his feet and looking down at his worn sneakers. "I'll tell you somethin' I ain't never told nobody before, Teach," he said softly.

"What's that?" I asked.

"Well . . . I used to think maybe I could be a doctor when I got grown. I used to dream about it and . . ." He grinned broadly at me. "But I was just snowin' myself, Teach. Bein' a doctor takes a lot of years of college and a lot of money."

"I worked my way through college, George, and so have a lot of very fine doctors."

"Yeah." His grin twisted crookedly. "But bein' a black man don't help none, Teach. You got everything against you before you even start."

"I know it isn't easy being a Negro, George," I said, "but life isn't easy for a *lot* of people, no matter what the color of their skin. And what matters most is not the color of a man's skin but the strength of his backbone. Any man can climb to the pinnacle of success if he has the backbone to get him there. But you've got to be willing to make sacrifices and to work hard."

The boy's face was sober, his eyes wide with interest as he slowly nodded. "Yes, sir . . ."

"And there's one other thing, George," I said. "As you climb toward that pinnacle, you've got to keep your head raised and your eyes looking upward, and you've got to believe with all your heart you're going to get there. Because if you believe in yourself, and you believe you'll make it, you will."

"Gee, Teach," he half-smiled, "nobody ever talked to me like that before. You know—it makes sense!"

The bell rang. "Think about it, George," I told him as he moved to his post by the door, and as the homeroom boys stormed in, I could tell by the grave look in his eyes that George was, indeed, thinking about it. *If only I could get some of the others to do the same thing,* I thought as Billy Parrish came sullenly in. He stood in front of George and deliberately spat on the floor.

George looked down at the smaller boy and said simply, in a flat voice, "Clean it up."

"Clean it up yourself," Billy sneered.

George grabbed him roughly by his shirt. "Now you listen to me, you no-good nigger trash," he said between clenched teeth. "I give you a shiner cause I got a gentle nature and I was goin' easy on you, see? But you gimme any more trouble, daddy-o, and I breaks you a bone!"

Seething with rage, Billy got a piece of paper and cleaned up his spit. Perhaps the Board of Education wouldn't approve of George's method of exacting discipline but I, personally, hoped that the boy who threatened to break bones would grow up to be a man who mended them.

Even though my Educational Study Guide outline said there should be three activities per day, I thought I'd try an experiment on my own. It had become quite clear that most of my students honestly did not know how to study. If I could teach them that basic principle, they would at least have a start in the right direction.

"Students, the foundation for education is proper study," I told my Period One group. "If you don't know how to study, you can't learn. It's that simple. Now, today, we're going to try a different method. It will give you an idea of what study actually is."

I was surprised for already they were quiet and seemed interested. Maybe that was part of the trick, I thought, something new and different. Even the most simple-minded person is always interested in something new and different.

"Open your texts to page thirty-one," I told them. "I'm going to read and you are going to listen. When I find something I think is important, I'll write it on the board and you copy it on your paper. When we're through, I'll give you time to look over your notes, and then we'll have a quiz."

Somebody groaned and a couple of them giggled but when I began reading, they all quieted down and listened attentively. They took notes from what I wrote on the board, and when we were through, I told them they would have ten minutes to review what they had written down.

Then Mr. Towers came in the back door. Smiling, he took a seat. Wryly, I thought, it was just like him to smell when I was doing something on my own, and come in to check. I hoped my experiment would at least be halfway successful so I could prove to him that a teacher's *individualistic* approach might have some worth, after all.

I told the students to put their books and notes away, and to take out a clean piece of paper. Then I wrote the quiz questions on the board. The chronic loafers were loafing but the majority of the students were busily at work. After ten minutes, I had them pass the papers to the front and I began grading them. My spirits soared as I quickly corrected.

"Well, we've got four perfect papers," I said happily, "and you all did well. Didn't I say you could do it if you tried? That's the difference—*trying!*"

Someone started applauding and the rest of the class followed suit. Mr. Towers sat there smiling below the disapproval in his eyes.

The bell rang and I was so excited over the results of my experiment that I didn't care how much noise the kids made as they left the room.

The Principal came to the front. "You're making it too tough on them, Mr. Brent," he said, still smiling. "I couldn't answer those questions you had on the board myself."

"Too tough?" I repeated in surprise. "But I got four perfect papers! I've never even had one before today."

He chuckled. "Perfect papers are fine, Brent, just fine,

but when are those kids going to have to know who the hell Queen Hatshepsut was?"

"Well, I don't know but . . ."

"If you don't know why they have to learn something, I don't know that you should teach them that, do you? Let's face it, digging into a lot of history is just a waste of time. Our new philosophy of education tries to give the children a generalized knowledge of history, but we've thrown out the old idea of making them learn a lot of names and dates. They can always look it up in a book if they have to. That's what I do."

"I guess we're all different, Mr. Towers," I said, frowning. "I believe that when I know history for myself, and I can look at tomorrow with a knowledge right in my mind of the past, I can act more wisely today."

He sighed deeply. "Brent, did you ever consider another calling—philosophy, perhaps?"

"No," I replied evenly.

"You should," he said and walked out of the room.

I felt like slugging him. But I knew as a teacher I was as powerless as a tiny tin soldier trying to battle the giant educational hierarchy and their "new philosophy of education," and just about as effective. But it would be worth losing many battles if only I, and teachers who believed as I did, won the war, and so-called progressive education was finally defeated. I remembered the Principal's words: "Progress means some sort of advancement or improvement . . ." My students had shown remarkable improvement with just one lesson using a new technique—actually, an old-school technique—and yet, because it wasn't in the book of rules set down by the progressive-minded hierarchy, it was met with disapproval. It was no wonder teachers lost their individualism and initiative. They had to follow orders and conform to group thinking whether it got results or not.

How naïve I had been when I appeared my very first day! How hopeful and idealistic! And already, after only a short period of experience, I was beginning to doubt working education as it stood. There were so many weaknesses in educational policies. The very atmosphere was too thick for me to breathe freely as a dedicated teacher. I was more like a mechanical man, an automaton. But was that actually what the great hierarchy wanted its teachers to be? "Buy the doughnuts and stick to the rules—for your own sake." Was that what I'd worked so hard to get my diploma for? Was that what I'd dedicated the rest of my life to?

By the time my last class of the day came in, I'd gone over those questions enough in my mind to come up with an answer. It was "No!"

It was *no* despite the fact that Principal Towers had sent me a note: "In case I did not make it entirely clear, you are not to continue with the method of teaching you used in Period One. You are to assign chapters for your pupils to read and give them generalized tests. You are to have three activities in each class period. Any more, we think, is a waste of time."

Ophelia Hernandez came in, sat down and, as usual, began staring quietly out the window. Johnny Dillon ran to his seat beside her and giggling, said, "Hey, Mexican bean! You always starin' up at the sky . . . you lookin' for God and angels with wings?"

"That's enough, Johnny," I ordered. Then a thought occurred to me. Johnny had handed in one of the best homework assignments of any student yet. Yet his record of achievement from other classes was barely passable. He was a good-natured boy and the only problem I'd had with him had been his laziness and slovenly work habits. Perhaps with a little extra help, and if he were willing to try, we might not only bring up his grades but instill some measure of interest in him to learn.

I called him to my desk, praised him for his perfect paper, and asked, "Would you like to stay after school and do a little extra work, Johnny? I'd be willing to help you—maybe you could get some good grades."

Grinning, he scratched his head uneasily. "Well, I don't know, Teach. I got this paper route, see, and—"

"What time do you go to work?"

" 'Round four."

"What about a half hour, Johnny? Let's just try working an extra half hour every day for a couple of weeks and see what happens. You might even get out of this class and into one of the more advanced groups."

He shook his head in disgust. "Well, I sure would like to get out of this here class, Teach. These kids are all buggy in the head."

I smiled. "Okay, then, shall we give it a try?"

He scratched his head again but before he could answer, Roger Gates came storming in. "Hey, Teach! Captain Smith is in the toilet, beatin' his meat like two skunks in a cabbage patch!"

The other students who were streaming in broke into one great roar of convulsive laughter. Slapping a ruler on the desk, I almost yelled for quiet. The laughter continued. I stood up. "By the time I get back to this room," I said loudly, "I want complete silence!"

I went quickly to the nearby rest room. And there he was. "Captain Smith!"

The boy froze in his self-absorbed activity and smiled sheepishly up at me. What could I say to him? How could I explain such a delicate matter to a retarded child in a limited time? My class would be bringing down the rafters if I didn't get back quickly.

I decided I'd better not try to explain. "Captain Smith, you're late for class," I said firmly. "Come with me."

Pouting, he buttoned his Levis and as we went back down the hall, I told him, "I'll give you a note which I want you to take to the nurse after school." But I wondered what I would tell the nurse. "Explain to Captain Smith that he is not supposed to masturbate on school time"? Then the anger surged up within me. This boy had no place in a regular public school! He simply did not belong there! And yet, I was supposed to pass him from B9 English! I was supposed to help him get a diploma! Such an educational system was not only disgusting, it was senseless.

As we got to the classroom door, the Captain went down on all fours and crawled in.

"Hey, Captain, don't you know you'll get snakes in your belly beatin' your meat like that?" Roger shouted hysterically and other smutty remarks immediately followed.

"You oughta get some cool chick to do it for you, Captain!"

"I bet it ain't no bigger'n my little finger!"

"I bet it ain't half as big!"

Captain Smith crawled for the Yellow Pages and then to his seat. I ordered quiet but they went right on with their noise. I had a strong urge to get my things and walk out of the school and never come back!

It took me a good five minutes to bring about some semblance of order but the class was disrupted for the day. I was barely able to keep them under control, and I breathed an exhausted sigh of relief when the closing bell rang.

I straightened my desk and was just leaving when I noticed that one of the students had dropped a notebook in the aisle. I picked it up and opened it. A sketch of a graveyard was painstakingly drawn on the first page. There were rows of tombstones. On each tombstone was printed a name: Geraldine Robinson, Radiation Burns, Marion Blackwell, Roger Gates, John Dillon, and so on. And in front of the rows was a single, large and ornately carved tombstone. On it was printed: Mr. Brent. Ugly reptilian creatures were crawling all over the grave, and what looked like a huge bat was perched on the crest of the stone.

I searched through the book for the owner's name. And I felt no surprise when I found it scrawled on the last page: Billy Parrish.

"Mr. Brent . . ."

I looked up. "Johnny . . ."

He grinned bashfully. "I—er—was just thinkin', Mr. Brent," he stammered. "If you really meant that I might get into a better class if I work after school, well, I reckon maybe . . . well . . ."

"Come in and sit down, Johnny," I said. "We'll begin work right away!"

6

The day began badly. I'd been up until almost four o'clock correcting papers. Report card time was approaching, and in trying to lift the students' grades I'd poured on extra work for them, which meant more work for myself.

Traffic snarled on the freeway and the bumper-to-bumper procession of steel crept through the thick smog. My eyes burned and watered, and thoughts of what was happening to education made me feel tears might well spring from the funeral services conducted some thirty years ago when progressive education policymakers put educational standards away to rest. The Sacramento hierarchy cracked the whip and the sister cities lined up as close as a chain reaction bumper smashup.

At last I arrived in the school parking lot. I looked at my watch. I had two minutes to make it to the register in the front office. I ran.

As I signed in, I looked up at the clock. I was one minute past the thirty-minute deadline before classes began.

"You're late, Mr. Brent," Principal Towers said with his smile. "What detained you?"

"Freeway jam."

"You'll have to get up earlier." He made a heavy check next to my name on the goof sheet.

I nodded and walked toward my homeroom. George Washington ran down the hall to meet me, grabbing my briefcase. "Hi, Teach," he said excitedly. "Say, my mother went to one of them Muslim meetings last night! The Muslims are going to do some terrible things to the white people!"

I wanted to avoid any conversation about the Muslim menace. As we walked into the homeroom, I said, "Smoggy day, George. I don't know whether it would clean the air in the room or make it worse if I opened a window."

But George went on excitedly. "You know, Teach, I don't believe in the Muslims. You're a good stud, and just cause your skin is white, I'm not going to hate you. You're white, I'm black, but you don't treat me bad, so I figures, why should I treat you bad? Just because you're white, I mean."

I smiled at him. "You're an intelligent boy, George."

The bell rang, and then came the morning stampede. After homeroom, my Period One class came in. I had decided a good topic would be: "What has the Negro contributed to American culture?" "Culture" would require explanation, I knew. And "contribution" would require explanation. But I wanted to help them understand they had a right to be proud in themselves as a race. Then perhaps they'd take the chips off their shoulders.

When I wrote the assignment on the board there were a lot of confused questions, as I'd expected. I explained the topic, ending with, "You should know some of the things the Negroes have done which make life a better one. It could be an invention. It could be something to do with music . . ."

A lot of "oh's," "ah's," and "ya's" rose from them and they began writing. All except a girl named Susie Mae who was gazing into a mirror, brushing her huge bubble hair-do, and intermittently taking big bites from a sandwich. Its gooey mayonnaise exuded unpleasantly from her thick lips. Its rancid odor came clear to my desk.

"School rules forbid any eating in the classroom," I said.

With a sigh of disgust, Susie Mae put the sandwich away. Then she picked up her mirror again, I looked quizzically at her reflection, and asked aloud, "What's wrong with me?" She then pulled out a piece of meat which had stuck between her front teeth and laughed loudly. Finally, she began writing.

After fifteen minutes, I picked up the papers and gave a reading assignment. Then I began reading:

"George Washington Carver, one Negro man who did

lots of things for America . . . peanuts, oil, milk, grease . . . all kinds of things."

"In my honest opinion, I really don't think that the Negro has given anything at all to the American culture."

In wildly scrawled handwriting, one boy wrote, "The Negro has given us a lot of Kulture."

"I think they can sing, dance, play, and share. But some steal."

"The Negroes have given huge families."

Another wrote unintelligibly, "He invented lipskit. I was a teacher, he was a teacher in a church, he was fat and blue eyes, he was a great man."

Someone wrote, "Marilyn Anderson."

One declared in bold print, "If it wasn't for the Negroes all the cotton would be rotting in the south."

I was amazed. They actually knew nothing of the achievements of their own race. When I was through reading, I told them of some outstanding Negroes and their gifts to the American scene. They listened intently, with eager eyes and smiles playing around their lips. I thought how wonderful it would be if they could permanently identify with this glistening, split-second of joy they were realizing as they came to know that the Negro had accomplished things any white man could envy. If only I could inspire them to aim high and forget their color, forget prejudice and hate, and remember they were human beings endowed with dignity, talent, opportunity and the capacity to accept challenge. If only I could get them to fight for a seat next to the intellectual giants of the ages on the bus open to all, true education, with the same fervor the Freedom Riders fought for a seat next to a white man on a bus.

Then I would know they were on the right highway to genuine equality.

As my Period One class faded away in a din of noise, another, stampeding and shoving, appeared. And on into the day. In each class, I repeated the same assignment. At first, there was a reluctant reaction to the topic, then gradual enthusiasm, accelerating into pride, when the positive parade of Negro achievements marched courageously through their papers, refusing to let the negative prejudice of notorious publicity distort the fact that all America had many things it could take pride in because of Negro achievement. Briefly, I thought that perhaps Helen and Mother could well do with such a lesson.

I wondered if my last class, the Special group, could handle such a topic. And yet, I knew they needed the positive self-image more than any of the other classes. I decided to give it a try, and if they could think of nothing on their own, I'd tell them stories of Negroes who had become world-famous for their true worth despite great handicaps. The bell rang and in came my problem people.

"Off the floor, Captain Smith," I ordered.

He paid no attention but, as usual, crawled across the room to the Yellow Pages. He took the heavy book to his desk where he dropped it with a thud, looking at me to see if I was going to be bait for his action. I said nothing.

Roger ran in and up to my desk. He shoved a magazine at me. It was EBONY "Teach, this here magazine says *Black Man In The White House!* That's what they call one of their stories, and that's race prejudice!"

"Hardly, Roger," I said, glancing through the magazine. "This article is about an outstanding Negro man who is a statesman in the White House."

"But it says *black* man in the *white* house!"

"What's wrong with that?"

"Black, Teach, *black!* They got no right to say black!"

I looked at the picture of the Negro statesman standing before the White House in Washington and I realized for the first time that the use of the word "black" did ignite the fires of belligerence in the Negro. And yet, EBONY was a Negro publication. I said as much to Roger.

"I don't care if it is Negro," he said narrowly. "I still say they're race-prejudiced!"

I sighed. "Roger, is there anyone you think isn't race-prejudiced?"

He got a sneaky, all-knowing look in his round eyes. "You don't know, Teach, you just don't know," he muttered, and, taking his magazine, went to his seat.

The bell rang and I got the class quieted down. Then I noticed that Captain Smith had vanished.

"Where is Captain Smith?" I asked.

"We threw him out the window," Billy Parrish sneered.

"That's enough, Billy!"

"The kids in San Fernando Valley threw a teacher out a second-story window," Billy announced evenly.

Without warning, the venetian blinds at the rear window crashed to the floor. I walked to the window and there was Captain Smith, untangling himself from the blinds. The kids jumped noisily out of their seats. Miss Joseph flung upon the door which connected our rooms. "What happened?" she called anxiously.

Captain Smith just sat there on the floor with his head

sticking up out of the blinds, laughing and laughing. Principal Towers appeared. *Good timing, old man,* I thought. *Another check for your goof sheet.* Miss Joseph quickly shut the door behind her.

"I was just walking by and heard a little noise." Towers spoke in the same even tone Billy had used when he told about throwing a teacher out the second-story window.

"Get back to your seats, everyone," I ordered, and returned to my desk.

Captain Smith finally emerged from the mangled blinds and for once, almost with dignity, *walked* back to his seat. Principal Towers sat down in the back of the room, clasped his hands on the desk, and looked around, the image of a stocky, smiling Buddha.

Marion Blackwell didn't return to her assigned seat. Instead, she plopped down in a seat next to the windows.

"Marion, sit in your own seat, please," I said.

She jumped up. "I'll sit where I damn please," she shouted defiantly.

The class sat in stunned silence, some of them sneaking glances at the Principal. Marion stared at me, her eyes glazed with unyielding will and lit with hate.

Mr. Towers rose. "What's the matter, Marion dear?"

The girl bowed her head. "I just want to sit near the window and Mr. Brent won't ever let me," she half-whimpered.

The Principal looked at me and said with a gracious tone and a gentle smile, "Now, Mr. Brent, it doesn't really make any difference if Marion sits near the window, does it?"

I hesitated, and before I could give a reply, he turned

back to the girl and asked, "Marion, will you promise to be a good girl if Mr. Brent lets you sit near the window?"

"Oh, yes, sir! That's all I ever wanted!" Flashing me a look of exultant triumph, Marion sat down in her unassigned seat.

Mr. Towers came up to my desk. "I'd like to see you after school, Brent," he said, and left the room.

Basking in Marion Blackwell's triumph, the class was once again almost uncontrollable. Even my stories of Negro achievements were scarcely listened to and I spent most of the period quieting them down.

When the bell rang and the class was gone, I walked to the window. A few trees were leafless, patio flowers hung limp, and the lawn was faded. I felt the chill dampness of the November air. And I thought about tomorrow. I knew that tomorrow, the kids would say, "Principal told Marion she could sit where she wanted to. Why can't I sit where I want to? I'm just as good as Marion!" With a sigh, I thought a teacher is only as strong as the administration which backs him up. Teachers need help in their disciplinary measures, not hinderance.

"Mr. Brent . . ."

I recognized the husky voice before I turned around. "What is it, Marion?" I asked, facing her.

"I just want you to know," she said, "I hate your guts!"

I frowned. "Why, Marion? Why?"

"Because you're white, that's why." She took a quick breath. "Did you ever hear of the Muslims?"

"Yes."

"Well, my folks are Muslims and I think you know what they think about you white trash!"

I breathed deeply. "Is that all, Marion?"

An evil smile played around her full lips. "No, that ain't all, Mr. Brent. There's gonna be a lot more. You wait. You'll see. We Muslims are gonna teach you white folks one thing for damn sure—to never say nigger!"

"I'm sorry you feel the way you do," I said earnestly. "Hate breeds hate, Marion. The Muslims can only make trouble for the Negroes because they preach color hate. And you're going to understand some day that you're wrong. I hope it isn't too painful a lesson."

She laughed drily. "You just wait, Mr. Brent. You'll get yours. You'll see." She turned and walked out of the room.

Wondering why Negroes like Marion and, obviously, her parents, didn't see that with their preaching of color hate, they were causing themselves trouble, I went down to the office and checked out. Then I went to Mr. Tower's office. He was busy with papers on his desk but when he looked up and saw me, he lit a cigarette, took a deep puff and leaned back in his chair.

"Brent, I hope you learned a little lesson from the experience with Marion Blackwell today," he said flatly.

"I want to talk to you about that," I said, controlling a sudden anger. "I don't want to conflict with your views, but if Marion has a right to sit where she wants to, then don't all the others have the right to sit where they want to? And what am I supposed to do if they all want to sit on the same seat?"

"Brent, you're always making a Federal case out of a traffic violation," he said with annoyance. "And in the case of Marion Blackwell, I want to warn you. When it's just a matter of a little give and a little take, give, Brent, give! Her folks are Muslims and I don't want to tangle with those people!"

"Are you afraid of them, Mr. Towers?" I asked angrily.

"No, I'm not afraid of them! I'm just being cautious!" He exploded. "You don't know these people the way I do! So just take my word for it—you'd better give!"

I took a deep breath. "Yes, sir," I said stiffly, and moved toward the door.

"Oh, and Brent . . ."

"Yes, sir?"

"That's an order!"

As I walked away, I thought there's still another element retarding true education. You could call it "cautious" or any other name you wanted to but what it boiled down to was simply fear. How could proper discipline be maintained and proper education be taught when there was a need for weapons checking among the students and favoritism shown to students whose parents belonged to a threatening organization? How could these kids grow up to be more than reflections of their parents' hates and hostilities if we didn't have the courage to discipline and teach them properly?

It was predicted that by 1980, the minorities—Negro, Mexican and Oriental—would be majorities in California's major cities, with the emphasis on the growth of the Negro population. The question in my mind was, how could educators fear them as children and not be wary of how they would act as adults and as a majority?

There was no doubt that education was the only answer. But how could we teachers truly educate when the administration standing behind us did not have the backbone we were trying to give the children?

There didn't seem to be any real, solid answer. And I wondered if my sister, Helen, might not be right. Perhaps I had not only bitten off a bigger bite than I could chew but a poisonous one.

7

The smog had drowned the sun. The traffic hadn't snarled on the freeway; it had simply stalled, and I could see less than a block ahead of me through the smut. It was 7:10 in the morning.

I turned on the radio for the traffic alert on the morning news report:

"Motorists are advised to take alternate routes on the Los Angeles Freeway, inbound. A thirty-five car collision has stalled traffic completely and it will be at least one hour, police estimate, before traffic moves normally . . .

A smog alert has been declared by the Los Angeles Smog Pollution Control. The density has reached the dangerous stage. Invalids and elderly people suffering heart or lung ailments are advised to stay in their homes and rest until the smog has lifted. The Governor has issued his morning statement that something will be done about the Los Angeles smog shortly. He suggests Los Angeles homeowners finance, through taxation, a Monorail which would eliminate the exhaust fumes from the cars . . ."

I switched stations. A jazz singer was bouncing *Rubber Balls.* Mr. Towers came to my mind and I could feel myself beginning to perspire. I wiped my forehead and sighed heavily. The result was a pain in my chest and the murky taste and sharp burning of smog in my lungs.

I switched stations again. . . . The Angeles Crest fire was still out of control. The ashes and smoke from the fire were causing a smog blackout and motorists were advised to stay off the Los Angeles Freeway for at least one hour, due to a thirty-five car collision . . .

I turned off the radio. I could see Mr. Towers smiling over the sign-in register. "Mr. Brent, a substitute is in your homeroom. I'd like to see you after school."

I could picture George Washington, in all his glory, standing like a sentinel at the door, ready to use his fists to solve all problems. I could hear the substitute teacher saying, "Class, Mr. Brent may let you get by with this but I won't!"

I could hear the students taking full advantage of the dig at me and maligning me with everything they could think of. "Mr. Brent's no good. He's scared to use the paddle." That would be Billy Parrish. With a touch of warmth, I hoped my loyal friend, George Washington, wouldn't defend my name with another sock in Billy's eye or then there would be another thing for Mr. Towers to berate me with. "Brent, you selected Washington to control the boys but Washington needs control himself! You've shown poor judgment!"

I half-smiled as I thought of my imaginary answer. "Mr. Towers, these kids seem to understand the language Washington uses better than the soft policies the Board of Education recommends."

"Mr. Brent! Do you mean to tell me your judgment is so twisted that you see right and wrong through the eyes of a black bully?"

"Mr. Towers!" Perhaps I would gasp a little in shock.

He would be chagrined. "Brent, I'm sorry. I didn't mean to say 'black.' It's just that . . . well . . . sometimes these kids exasperate me! Sometimes it's just more than I can stand!"

The traffic began moving and my daydream came to an end. I turned the ignition back on. I was afraid to look at my watch. I just listened to the steady ticking in my brain: "Brent, you're late . . . Brent, you're late . . . Brent, you're late . . ." Again.

And of course, Principal Towers was standing at the sign-in register when I arrived in the front office. "Brent, you're very late. What detained you?"

"Freeway smash-up," I said, hastily signing in.

"Well, hurry on to your class. I sent someone to substitute for you."

In my homeroom, George Washington was standing by the door, rigid and resolute. The students were quiet. The bell rang just after I walked in and the substitute hastily excused himself and exited.

The periods slid noisily by. During my fifteen minute lunch period, I wondered what I could do to hold the interest of my Special group today. If they could be doing something with their hands, they might have some feeling of accomplishment, but the law was the law, and these kids had to be confined in classroom whether or not they could do anything scholastically. I wondered what would happen if I asked them what they wanted to be when they became adults. Surely they must have dreams, secret desires. If they would open up and let me know what they wanted in life then perhaps I might be able to help them try to use their school work to achieve their goals.

By the time the last class arrived, I had definitely decided to try this tactic. The students began arriving. Angelina was wearing one of her peasant blouses. One sleeve was pushed down almost to the elbow, revealing a voluptuous cleavage between her weighty breasts. The boys were giggling with their eyes fixed and Angelina was in her glory.

Captain Smith crawled in. I didn't react to him so he got to his feet and ran around the room.

"Sit down, Smith," I ordered.

Running around the room once more, he grabbed the Yellow Pages as he went by and collapsed at his desk, grinning toothily, and strangely with innocence.

Geraldine Robinson walked in laughing with Roger Gates. Ophelia Hernandez slipped quietly in the back door. Finally, the students had all taken their seats. Just as the bell rang, Marion Blackwell came in and walked to the seat Principal Towers allowed her to have. I said nothing.

When I got them quieted, I told them that today they were going to write on what they'd like to be when they became adults. I told them they could read to the class what they'd written.

After about ten minutes of writing, Roger Gates waved his hand frantically. "Can I read now, Teach?" he asked.

I told him he could and he came quickly to the front of the room. Then he doubled with laughter.

Firmly, I said, "Roger, if you can't control yourself, sit down."

"Okay, Teach," he said, straightening. Then he began reading. "I wanna be a cool doctor, a chick's specialist. There's a certain cure that'll help all women. They'll come in and say, 'Something's wrong with me' and I'll say, 'I'll look inside you and feel—"

"That's enough, Roger," I interrupted harshly.

The class broke into laughter. Giggling, Roger returned to his seat.

Billy Parrish waved his hand. "Let me read mine!"

"Okay, Billy," I said, dreading it, and wishing I had never given such an assignment.

Billy came to the front of the room. "I want to be a playboy," he read solemnly. "I want the lame girls to whip on me and travel around the world. I'll have a Chinese kick in Hong Kong and a—"

"Billy! Go back to your seat!"

Amid the laughter, the boy grudgingly returned to his desk. I stood up, angry and disgusted. "If another one of you comes up here and reads this sort of thing, I'll send you to the Principal! Don't you want to amount to something when you grow up?"

Every hand went up in a show of understanding except Billy Parrish's and Marion Blackwell's. I started to speak to the girl but Mr. Towers' warning insinuated itself into my mind. Feeling some degree of guilt for my small cowardice, I called upon Captain Smith.

"I'm gonna be a garbage man and eat the garbage," he shouted. The class buckled in laughter, and the captain laughed the loudest.

Angelina jumped up. "I'm gonna marry a private dick," she yelled jubilantly, "and help increase the population!"

The class shrieked. I cried out vehemently, "Angelina, you're going to Mr. Towers!"

The girl screamed, "Fuck you," half in laughter and half in rage.

Pulling every nerve taut in an effort to control my own rage, I walked slowly to her desk. The class was suddenly, warily silent. I looked into the girl's blazing eyes. I never wanted to grab someone and shake him as much as I wanted to shake the filth out of that foul-tongued girl.

"Come with me," I said in a flat but firm voice. "We are going to the Principal."

She went phonily saccharine. "Aw, forget it, Mr. Brent, please! I promise I'll never say another dirty word again. I just don't know what came over me, honest!"

"Come with me."

I asked Miss Joseph to watch the class for me. "Trouble?" she asked sympathetically.

"I'm beginning to think there's nothing but trouble with these kids," I sighed.

"I know what you mean." She shrugged. "But if I were you, I wouldn't make too much of an issue out of it. These days, you know, the teacher is hardly ever right."

When we got down to the Principal's I told Angelina to wait in the outer office and I went into the inner sanctum alone.

"Well, what's wrong this time, Mr. Brent?" Towers asked heavily.

"I know you said you didn't have time to bother with every child who said a dirty word, Mr. Towers, but I think what just happened in my classroom requires your attention. I have to put an end to the filthy talk which constantly goes on in my Special group. I have one of them in the outer office who—"

"You simply are not communicating, Brent," Towers interrupted sharply. "That's all there is to it. You are not communicating!"

"I've got to have some backing, Mr. Towers," I said heatedly. "I can't—"

"Some people are born teachers. The kids just fall in line. Other people want to be teachers but they just can't make the grade. Unfortunately, it seems that you fall into the latter category."

My anger flamed toward the exploding point. But I clenched my fists and managed to speak evenly. "That may be your opinion, Mr. Towers, but my concern right now is stopping once and for all the filthy language used in my classroom. The children have no respect for my authority. Perhaps they will for yours."

He sat back, groaning a weary sigh. "All right, Brent. Send him in. I'll give him a talking to."

"It's not a him," I said. "It's a her."

"And what terrible, filthy word is she guilty of using?" he asked with more than a trace of sarcasm.

" 'Fuck you,' Mr. Towers," I said flatly, and I must admit, I got some feeling of satisfaction out of saying it.

I went back to my classroom, thanked Miss Joseph, and slapping the ruler on the desk for quiet, said, "Class, I want to bring a very important matter to your attention. You make yourselves what you are by the way you think. And when you talk and act, you reveal what you think, and therefore, the kind of person you really are. If you use filthy language when you talk, then you must be a filthy person, inside."

Billy Parrish raised his hand. "The gym teacher uses dirty talk," he announced gloatingly. "He told me, 'Billy Parrish, you get your goddamn hands off that girl,' and when I didn't, he called me a son of a bitch and he—"

"That's enough!"

"My old man cusses all the time," shouted Geraldine.

"So does mine," cried Roger.

"You oughta hear how my ma cusses me when—"

"Class, *that is enough!*" They silenced and I asked, "How many of you go to church?"

Every student raised his hand.

"Very well. If you go to church that means you believe in God, right?"

In unison, they cried, "Right!"

"Well, then, do you think God wants you speaking the

way you have been today? Do you think He would approve of the way you've acted?"

Captain Smith waved his hand frantically. "But the preacher, he say God done forgive all our sins!"

"Yeah, but that don't mean He forgets 'em!" Johnny Dillon cried out.

The door opened. With bowed head, Angelina came in and went quietly to her seat. I looked at the clock. It was one minute before the final bell. I turned back to the class just in time to see Billy Parrish stick his leg out and kick Ophelia Hernandez who sat in front of him.

Ophelia reeled with pain, grabbing her ankle, then with tears in her eyes, she swung around and yelled, "You, Billy Parrish, you go fuck yourself!"

"Ophelia!" I blurted in surprise.

"You're a dirty, rotten nigger, Billy Parrish," Ophelia cried brokenly.

"Don't you never say nigger," Marion Blackwell yelled.

Angelina jumped up excitedly. "She said a filthy word! Mr. Brent, Ophelia said the same filthy word I said!"

"She called me a nigger," Billy yelled angrily. "Yeah, she did, Mr. Brent."

"If I went to the Principal, that Mexican bean has gotta go too," Angelina cried, "She said 'fuck' just like I did!"

The closing bell rang. Wondering briefly how to handle the situation, I rose. "Class dismissed," I said. "Ophelia, stay for a moment, please. I'd like to have a word with you."

"You mean you ain't gonna send her to the Principal?" Angelina shouted.

"I said, class dismissed!"

Most of the students raced out. Ophelia sat at her desk, her face in her hands, sobbing quietly. Angelina stalked up to my desk. "I asked you, you gonna send that Mexican bean to the Principal or not?"

"No, Angelina, I am not going to send Ophelia to the Principal.

She stared at me with absolute loathing. "I said 'fuck you' and you made me go. I'm a Negro. She said 'go fuck yourself' and you let her off. She ain't a Negro. You're race-prejudiced, that's what you are!"

Marion Blackwell leaned across my desk and practically spat, "Hateful, spiteful, mean, nasty, and race-prejudiced! You heard her say 'fuck' and you heard her say 'nigger'!"

"You are both dismissed," I said firmly.

Arm-in-arm, the two girls left the room. I felt I was being slowly broiled in the fires of white-hot hate. The sad and frustrating part of it was that it was not a momentary hate, flashing like a meteor through the sky of these children's feelings. It was a deep, intense hostility against my color. I recalled a story about a bear who came across a campfire in the forest. On the fire was a large kettle of boiling water. He picked it up and was seared with pain. He hugged the kettle to him because hugging was his natural method of fighting. And the harder he hugged, the greater was his pain. He had no way of knowing that until he threw the kettle away from him the pain would continue. How like the bear were these people! If only they could be made to understand that until they threw away their hates and hostilities, their pain would never cease.

I looked at Ophelia, wiping the tears from her eyes with the sleeve of her faded, worn dress. I knew she had spoken as she did only in a reaction to shock and pain. It was not a habit with her, and I had never heard her speak in any way other than quietly and respectfully. It was not correct that she should be disciplined in the same manner as Angelina who used filthy language constantly and deliberately. But I couldn't explain this to Angelina. Her mind was closed against understanding. She didn't want to understand. Like the bear, she was hugging her pain tightly to her and refused to let it go.

I went back and talked quietly with Ophelia, telling her I understood her reaction although I certainly didn't approve of it. I gave her a homework assignment as discipline and dismissed her.

As I left school that day, I thought, the smog is like their hate, too. Until it lifts, they will never be able to see truly and breathe freely.

8

About ten minutes before the closing of my Period Three class, several days later, the door opened and a woman of medium height and sallow face came in. She stood rigidly a moment, her piercing eyes darting around the room, then with a disapproving frown on her face, she came toward me. "I'm the district supervisor," she announced in clipped tones. Then focusing her beady stare on a student in the front row, she asked, "Who are you?"

The girl jumped. "Er—Elaine Stephens," she murmured.

"Elaine Stephens, take that gum out of your mouth this instant!"

Elaine quickly rolled her gum into a sheet of paper. The district supervisor nodded curtly and moved to a chair by the window. She sat down stiffly, her sharp eyes on the class. I didn't know what it was all about so I simply ordered the class to finish their assignments.

When the bell rang and the children had streamed out, the woman came toward me as if she were making a frontal attack on the enemy. "Mr. Brent, I understand you have very poor control of your students," she said crisply.

"Some of my students are rather difficult to control, Miss . . ."

She did not give me her name. With narrowed eyes, she said, "Please, Mr. Brent, don't try to rationalize this ugly situation. Don't try to blame the children for your inability to control them. If you motivated them properly, I'm sure they would perform wonders for you."

"Oh, they perform wonders for me, all right. All the time," I said with ill-clocked sarcasm which she chose to ignore.

She took a thick set of stapled papers from her bulky briefcase. "These are Lesson Plans. You are to type out five Lesson Plans every day. One for each class."

"Five a day? Why, that means twenty-five a week. . . five hundred a semester . . . a thousand a year!"

"I am well aware what it means, Mr. Brent," she said coldly. "Also . . . your bulletin boards are bad. Very, very bad. You should hang all your pictures evenly, never at angles. This is very important. And you must always use straight pins. Thumbtacks are distracting, we are told, very distracting."

I wanted to laugh. But it was probably lucky for me I didn't get a chance. The district supervisor said briskly on her way to the door, "And I'd seriously advise you to give thought to motivation, Mr. Brent. Good day."

I sighed into my chair and then allowed myself a little laugh. But there was also little humor in it. I must give daily ten minute writings in all my five classes. Then I had the English notebooks, with three book reports, the short stories, and my rollbook grades, I had to evaluate homework assignments three times a week for each student and record them. I had one hundred and fifty students. If I gave each one three grades a week that would be a total of four hundred and fifty grades a week. With twenty weeks in the semester, that would be nine thousand grades per semester. And two semesters in the school year meant I must give eighteen thousand grades a year!

And of course, I mustn't forget how very important it was to hang my pictures straight and to use straight pins instead of thumbtacks!

Roger Gates came running into the room. "Hiya, Mr. Brent! And how is you today, if I might be so bold as to ask?"

I couldn't help smiling. Roger would probably make one of the greatest con men in history by the time he was twenty-nine. "What are you doing here, Roger? This isn't your class."

The sly look came into his eyes. He glanced cautiously over both shoulders then sidled up to me. "You hear the rumble about Geraldine?" he asked, much sotto voce.

"No, I have not heard the rumble about Geraldine," I said.

"Well, last night, she went with these six studs, see, and they went over to the closed grocery store one of 'ems old man owns and they all—now get *this,* Mr. Brent, Teach, sir—they all took turns and—"

"That's enough, Roger," I interrupted with a sigh. "I'm not interested in any of the dirty—"

"Okay, okay! Don't get your bowels in an uproar!" He giggled. "I just thought you might wanta know who's screwin' who and how many?"

"Roger, why can't you get your mind out of the gutter?" I asked. "You have average intelligence. If you used your mind to learn your school work instead of spreading the filth you hear, you might find yourself in one of the advanced classes."

"Not me," he winked. "I don't wanta be in any advanced class."

"Why not? Don't you want to get ahead in life?"

"Oh, I'll get ahead okay, Teach," he laughed. "I'm sly."

"Sly?"

He nodded, grinning broadly. "I know how to use my brain to make me a fast buck when I want to. What do I need to learn boring old school work for?"

"All right, Roger," I said flatly. "Go to your class."

"Okay. See you later, Alligator."

Scarcely realizing it, I finished the chant. . . . "After awhile, crocodile."

My Period Four class had been streaming in and were now seated and quiet. For several days, most of my classes had been peopled with little angels. They had good reason—the close approach of Report Card Day. It was a day I looked forward to with dread. The Principal had said that if one kid was flunked, the teacher was failing himself. Regardless of his belief, I knew I had to fail some of my students. It would be totally unethical for me to pass them when they maintained such a low standard of grades.

With trepidation, I made out the report cards the following night. To the great majority of my students, I gave D's on their letter grades and unsatisfactory for effort and cooperation. And as I'd expected, when I gave the cards out the next day, I received a lot of angry arguments.

Geraldine didn't argue with me. She tried to bribe me. Before any of the other students arrived, she came hurrying into class. "Hi, Mr. Brent," she said, smiling broadly.

"Hello, Geraldine. You're not only on time today, you're early."

She came up to my desk and leaned across it, allowing her low-necked dress to fall open, revealing the contour of huge, unbrassiered breasts. "What you give me on my report card, Mr. Brent?" she asked softly. "You give me an A?"

"No, Geraldine, I didn't. You failed your final exam and you never do your school work in class. I'm afraid I had to give you an F."

"Mr. Brent!" She jerked upright. "I don't deserve no F!"

"Yes, you do, Geraldine."

She hesitated a moment and I could almost see the wheels turning in her head. Smiling, she came around the desk and leaned over. She put an arm around my shoulders. "Aw, now, Mr. Brent," she whispered huskily in my ear. "I can be real nice to somebody who treats me nice. Why don't you just make out another report card for me and give me a—"

"Go to your seat, Geraldine," I ordered firmly.

"I'll do anything, Mr. Brent, you want me to! I can take it backwards or—"

"Go to your seat!"

She stormed to her desk. But the scene wasn't over. When the bell rang and the other students were seated, she deliberately took a handful of pencils and walked to the pencil sharpener in the back of the room. I ordered her to sit down. She slowly began sharpening the pencils. The class laughed happily at her defiance.

I walked toward her. "Geraldine, I told you to take your seat." She whipped around, undulating toward me. I moved to the right. She followed my move as if she were dancing. I moved to the left. She followed. Then suddenly, pressing her body close to mine, we collided. The class burst out laughing.

"You got fresh with her, Mr. Brent," shouted Captain ing tauntingly.

"You got fresh with her, Mr. Brent," shouted Captain Smith.

Geraldine eased up to me again. "You sure don't dare flunk me now as I've got witnesses you been fresh, do you, Mr. Brent?"

Angelina yelled, almost fanatically, "Geraldine is a cute chick and you got fresh with her! I seen you and I'm her witness!"

"Geraldine is a whorin' bitch," Billy Parrish said loudly, "and she's always askin' for it!"

Geraldine whirled angrily. "Why, you no good black nigger—"

"Stop it!" I found myself shouting. "I'll send every one of you to the Principal!"

It was a hollow threat but they didn't know it. They muttered into quiet. Geraldine sullenly took her seat, and I gave out the report cards. I received the worst protests from my worst students.

"I ain't gonna take this crap lyin' down," Angelina loudly told Roger Gates. "I don't deserve no D."

Roger shrugged, grinned, and said, "So what's the diff?"

Johnny Dillon beamed his happiness and leaned over to say to Ophelia, "I ain't ever in my whole life got a report card this good!"

I saw Geraldine take a fountain pen and obviously sign her parent's name on the card.

From the others, grumblings, mutterings, and a few vicious arguments. The entire class, except for Johnny, thought I had graded them unfairly. The words, "race-prejudiced" went through the room like a tonic salving their injured pride.

Billy Parrish said nothing. He just sat there staring at me with the familiar look of homicidal hate in his eyes.

Just before the class ended, I received a note from the Principal. He wanted to see me after school. And I was not fool enough to think he wanted to praise me for giving my students the grades they deserved.

After closing, I went to see him. I sat opposite him, and he began by observing candidly, "In going over your grades, Mr. Brent, I have noticed that you gave exceptionally low ones."

"They were fair," I replied.

He spent awhile smiling, then said, "Mr. Brent, if you'd provide the right environment, you wouldn't have so many low grades. As I said before, you simply must not be communicating."

I could feel my muscles tighten. "The district supervisor called it motivation."

He nodded solemnly. "Well, that's a good word . . ."

"The fact is, Mr. Towers, that I spend hours on Lesson Plans. I spend hours on assignments. I supply pencils and paper because most of my students do not remember or do not care enough to bring them. I volunteer extra help to any student who wants it. And yet, they still do D work. I believe, in fact, that I'm being more than generous by giving them D's."

He produced the school handbook from a drawer in his desk and quoted, "The pupil with limited ability, who tries hard, might well receive a C, even though the quality of the work is poor."

"I am not a mind-reader, Mr. Towers," I said shortly. "I cannot guess whether a child is trying hard or not. I have simply their work to judge them by."

"We give the students I.Q. tests, Brent," he said with impatience. "You are supposed to put their I.Q. next to their name in your rollbook. When you grade them, you can then determine if they are working up to their capacity. If the I.Q. tests show they don't have much potential, you must be generous, Mr. Brent. Give them a C, even if their work is poor. The important thing is that they try hard."

"I think the I.Q. tests have their place," I said, "but how much value do they have with the kind of kids we're working with? Their native background, their entire culture, their lifelong training, can give the lie to the I.Q. test!"

He half-smiled. "You are always so technical, Mr. Brent."

"My point is, Mr. Towers, that if we let one kid get by just because he tries hard, then all the kids have a right just to 'get by'—despite how much their potential is and despite how bad their work is!"

Casually, he asked, "How long have you been teaching, Brent?"

"You know this is my first year."

"Well, then, don't you think you should wait until you've had a little more experience before you judge the policy of your superiors?"

"I'm sorry you interpret my observations and opinions as rebellion," I answered evenly, "but I can't help feeling that we're not doing all we can to help the kids get the best education possible. We're failing our young people, Mr. Towers."

"In what way are we failing them, may I ask?" He spoke as if I had given him a personal affront.

"We're turning them out ill-prepared to get a job. They have only rudimentary knowledge of basic skills . . . reading, writing and arithmetic. How are they going to get a job that's going to mean anything to them?"

"Well, I hardly think it's that bad. You're making a mountain out of a—"

"I recently read a report released by the National Education Association. They predict that the Negroes, the Mexicans, and the whites from the Appalachian Highlands will pose a terrible problem in just ten years when fifty per cent of our major cities will be inhabited by ignorant, illiterate people! Unless we reverse our progressive educational policies and go back to some concrete standards, our young people have no future!" I sat back and added flatly, "It's human nature to get by if you can, and I feel that it's up to us as educators not to let these kids just get by."

"Isn't it better to let them just get by than to keep them back?" he asked, frowning.

"They are keeping themselves back! I took a survey to find out how much time the average student watches television. It came to an average of fifty-two hours per week per student! One girl even said she watched it one hundred and thirty-two hours in one week! If we give them good grades for poor work when they're not even trying to—"

"It's pointless to argue about it, Brent," he interrupted shortly, rising. "As far as I am concerned—and *I* am the principal here, Mr. Brent—your grades represent a lack of communication. And I'd advise you to concern yourself less with so-called 'reports' and more with stimulating the minds of your students. Good afternoon."

I walked out of his office with a gnawing sense of defeat. Why couldn't I make him understand? Or were my ideals, my beliefs, without validity after all? Was I the one who was out of step in the educational army of my age?

A small group of Negro girls stood at the end of the hall. When they saw me coming, they began giggling and whispering.

As I started to pass them, Angelina stepped forward and asked brazenly, "are you gonna get fired, Mr. Brent, *sir?*"

I went on, ignoring the question, and as I moved down

the steps. I heard her shout defiantly, "You're no good as a teacher and you're race-prejudiced! And we're gonna get you fired! You wait, you'll see!"

I went on briskly, out the door, across the school yard. Every effort I made to reach these children was thwarted by their hatred for me. "Why? It must be more than just the color of my skin. There were other white teachers in the school. They didn't seem to have the trouble I had. Could it be because I required them to demand more of themselves than just getting by? Was it because I tried to put a dream of a better life in their hearts . . . a dream that would take effort and courage to make come true . . . when it took nothing from them to stay within the prison of their present lives?

Miss Joseph was standing beside my car, looking at the front tire. As I approached her, I saw why. All four tires had been slashed.

"You're just lucky they didn't put sugar in your gas tank," she said with doubtful optimism. "They did that to a couple of teachers last year. What did you do, flunk a lot of them?"

"No," I replied, "but I gave a lot of D's."

She shook her head. "They hate D's and C's. They're anxious to be smart and they want A's and B's to prove they're smart."

"But they're not willing to work for them!" I felt my anger mounting again.

"I know," she said easily. "I should have flunked half my students but who wants to get fired?"

I looked at her curiously, "Fired?"

She shrugged. "If you give too many low grades, you get a word of warning. If you flunk, you get fired. So if you put any value on your job, Mr. Brent, I'd advise you to let them all think they're smart."

"Miss Joseph, I put more value on my integrity as a teacher than I do on my job."

"You'll get over that." She smiled knowingly. "You know the old saying, 'you can't fight city hall'? Well, you can't fight the administration, either."

I watched her thoughtfully as she got into her car and drove off. And to myself, I thought, *maybe I can't fight the administration but I sure could wrestle with them!*

For the rest of the afternoon, while seeing about my car, having a solitary dinner in the cafeteria, and going back to the apartment, my anger stayed with me. When I began correcting papers, I found I couldn't concentrate. Nor could I concentrate when I tried to read. Finally, I knew I had to do something. I put on my tie and coat, and went in search of the hate-and-malice-filled young human being who had slashed my very good tires!

First, I drove to Johnny Dillon's home. I knew he had no ax to grind with me, and I thought perhaps he'd pass on any information he might know. At least, it was worth a stab—or a slash, I thought ironically, as I walked up the rickety wooden steps to the two-story apartment house.

I hunted for the name of Dillon but couldn't find it. I tapped on the torn screen door of the lower right-hand apartment.

"Who is it?" A woman's voice called out.

"I'm trying to find Johnny Dillon," I called back. "Do you know which apartment he lives in?"

There was a momentary silence, then an enormous Negro lady came to the screen and peered out at me suspiciously. "Whadda you want with Johnny Dillon?" she asked.

"I'm one of his teachers."

"Which one?" her eyes narrowed.

"Mr. Brent."

Her face broke into a smile. "Oh, Mr. Brent! Come in, Mr. Brent!"

I followed her through an old-fashioned dining room where a huge glass bowl was suspended from the ceiling from dingy, metal chains. It hung over an antiquated dining room table. In the living room, it was quite dark, with the only light coming from the television. She indicated the sofa with a wave of her hand and I sat down, the sofa springs unpleasantly poking me.

The woman sat in a straight wooden chair, stared at me anxiously, then asked, "Has Johnny done something wrong, Mr. Brent?"

"Not at all," I told her quickly. "He's doing good work now and I'm quite pleased with him."

She began to chuckle. "Well, I tell you, I was mighty pleased myself when he brought home that report card today! My sister got that child out of wedlock and I been wonderin' ever since if he'd come to any good."

She went on to give me a rather singular briefing of her younger sister's exploits with the opposite sex but she was so honestly naïve and without condemnation that it was completely unoffensive. She told me that she, herself, was a "re'lar prude. Or as Johnny says," she laughed deeply, "a square!" She made it clear how much she loved Johnny and how happy she was to have him live with her. She worked in a laundry to support them.

"Well, you can be very proud of Johnny," I smiled. "He wants to better himself."

Johnny must have been eavesdropping because he suddenly popped into the room, grinning, "Hi, Mr. Brent, sir!"

I told the boy and his aunt my reason for coming. Johnny had not known about my tires being slashed and he became amost wrathful. "I'd just like to get my hands on the stud that did that to you, Mr. Brent, sir!"

"No, Johnny," I said, rising. "If you should find out who did it, don't pick a fight. Just come and tell me. Okay?"

They followed me to the door and, taking my hand, Johnny's aunt said with deep sincerity, "You're a Christian man, a good man, Mr. Brent. Nobody ever tried to help my Johnny in school like you. Maybe because of you, he's gonna amount to something . . ."

I smiled at Johnny. "He's going to amount to something, and you know why?"

"Why, sir?" she asked humbly.

"Because he's *trying* to amount to something. That's the first and most important step a person can make."

As I walked back down the steps, I could hear the woman effusively telling Johnny of her pride in him. And I was very glad I'd come here. Much more important than finding the slasher of my tires was the instillment of faith, hope, and courage in deserving human beings.

And as I got into my car, I found, too, that some of my anger had dwindled away. I could see my own motivation more clearly. I didn't want to find the culprit who had slashed my tires simply to punish him, to make him pay for what he had done. I wanted to show him—and all the others—that he couldn't "get by" with an act of violence any more than I'd let him or any of them just "get by" without trying to make good grades.

Whispering aloud, I affirmed my belief in my ideals and myself. "It is up to us as educators and adults not to let these children get by with anything!"

I decided to call upon Geraldine Robinson. Despite the girl's actions that day, I still felt that basically, she wanted to do the right thing but she just didn't know right from wrong. She was attractive, with a pretty, soft face, and a voluptuous figure, and if she had not been taught that it was wrong to use these assets to try to get what she wanted, then it certainly wasn't her fault. I felt that with proper counseling she had the native intelligence to better herself, and I thought that perhaps some natural instinct for right might lead her to tell me the truth if she knew it.

Her address led me to the worst slum district downtown. She lived in quarters above a liquor store, a poolroom, and a pawnshop. I knocked on the door several times before a Negro man in filthy khaki pants and an undershirt opened it. His face was puffy, his lips and eyes swollen, and his hands were noticeably shaking.

He stared at me suspiciously and said nothing.

"Mr. Robinson?" I asked.

He nodded.

"I'm Mr. Brent, Geraldine's teacher at school."

He still said nothing.

"Is Geraldine at home?"

He shook his head.

"Are you expecting her?"

"Yeah!"

I wanted to step back from his breath, which reeked of the awful, stale odor of whiskey. "Well, I'd like to talk with her. May I wait?"

His face screwed up as if he were trying to focus his mind on some intelligible thought, then he said, "What you say your name was?"

"Brent, I'm one of Geraldine's teachers. And I'd like to talk with her."

He became suddenly angry. "I don't know when she be back but she better be soon. I tell you that! And she better bring that seventy-six cents with her, too! I needs that bottle of muscatel, and it ain't much to ask when I uses all my Federal aid to pay the rent and—"

I interrupted. "Well, I don't think I'll wait. It wasn't really important." I turned away and went down the hall.

"Who you say you were?" I heard him ask questioningly as I ran down the steps.

The smell of stale whiskey stayed with me until I was in my car and driving, and not until then did the sickening feeling in my stomach go away. Then I began to wonder. Her father had sent Geraldine out to get seventy-six cents for a bottle of muscatel. How did he expect her to get it?

I certainly couldn't divine the answer, so I deliberately turned my depressing thoughts away from Geraldine.

I thought about giving up my quest, then Franklin Williams came to my mind. Franklin was in one of the highly advanced groups, and I felt he had an exceptionally brilliant mind. He was absent more than he was present and yet, he always got good grades. I knew he must wing through his studies but it took an exceptional mind to be able to do that. If he were present more often there might be no limit to his capabilities.

I decided to call upon the boy, not so much to ask his help in finding my unholy culprit as to find out the reason for his constant absenteeism, and perhaps to encourage him to do better.

His address was on Humboldt Avenue. There were a series of small frame bungalows. His was the last one in the back. I rapped on the door and waited. I rapped again. There was no response and I started to leave, then Franklin opened the door. He was clad only in shorts, and he stared at me vacuously, as if he didn't know who I was.

"Mr. Brent, Franklin," I said. "You've been absent several days again. Are you sick?"

His eyes slowly focused and he smiled slightly. "Hi, Mr. Brent. Yeah, I've sorta been sorta sick, I guess."

"May I come in and talk with you?"

He hesitated, then with a shrug, said, "Why not?"

I went inside. The room was very dark. One small lamp glowed eerily with a blue bulb. In front of an artificial fireplace, a gas burner was flickering high, giving the place a stifling heat and a smothering, gaseous odor. I sat down on the sofa and it gave way to the floor where a leg was missing. Franklin slumped into a chair, throwing one leg over the side of its overstuffed arm. He yawned noisily.

"You've been absent a great deal this year," I told

him. "Despite that, your report card from me is good. I gave you a B. I was sorry you weren't there to get it today."

He grinned lopsidedly. "Thanks, Teach."

"Don't thank me, Franklin. I only gave you what you deserved. But I feel that if you were at school more often, you'd undeniably get all A's. You're an exceptional student."

"Yeah." He went on grinning in a silly fashion.

"Is there something chronically wrong with you, Franklin?" I asked seriously.

The door opened and one of the most unbelieveable scenes I could ever imagine took place. A girl came into the room. She was Negro, small and plump. And there was no doubt about her plumpness because she was totally nude. I sat, stunned, while her eyes slowly looked me over. Then she moved toward me in a serpentine fashion and asked huskily, "Franklin, he come to the party?"

Franklin laughed softly. "No, but maybe he might want to. You want me to ask him?"

"Yeah . . ." the girl murmured, continuing to move toward me.

Franklin lazily smiled at me. "You wanta get your balls off with one of my broads?"

I couldn't speak. I couldn't believe what I was seeing . . . not only Franklin and the nude girl but what was partially revealed through the open bedroom door . . . a naked Negro boy and Negro girl engaged in intercourse . . . a Negro boy pounding on bongo drums . . . and a red-haired mulatto girl executing a sensuous dance.

The nude girl moved with sudden quickness. Before

I realized what was happening, she had slithered into my lap and was pulling my face toward her's. "Come on, honey . . ."

I came to life, angrily pushing her away. She staggered backwards.

"What's the matter, Teach?" Franklin asked narrowly. "Ain't a black broad good enough for you? You wouldn't be shovin' away a naked white one, now, would you?"

"Franklin, what in hell is going on here?" I asked heatedly.

Franklin burst out laughing. "I thought you were smart, Mr. Brent, but you must be pretty dumb to pass up a hell of a good piece of mighty tight ass like Clorinda here!"

I moved toward the door. As I opened it, I heard the boy laugh giddily and, pulling down his shorts, he grabbed the girl and giggled, "Come on, let's show 'im how it's done, baby! Maybe he don't know!"

I stood for a moment in the fresh air wondering if I had actually witnessed such a spectacle or simply dreamed about it in my cluttered mind. They were merely children! Franklin couldn't have been more than fifteen, and the others appeared to be his age. And yet, I had never seen and certainly never even dreamed that such orgies ever took place. I'd read about them, in magazine articles and in newspapers, but they had always struck me as being part of some nether world which was completely out of touch with the world in which I lived. But this was my world! And I had seen what could not be interpreted as anything but a sexual orgy among children!

I wondered why there had been no fear, no cover-up,

from Franklin in my presence but any answer was beyond my ken. I drove to the nearest gas station and went into the telephone booth. I phoned the juvenile detail of the Los Angeles Police Department.

I was connected with a man by the name of Swartz. I told him what had happened, adding, "There's something besides a sex orgy going on there, Lieutenant. Franklin and the girl seemed to be in some dream world."

"Marijuana," he said flatly. "I'll leave right away. Meet me in front of the place."

Less than five minutes after I'd gone back, Lieutenant Swartz arrived with two other plainclothesmen. He was a big man with a hard jaw, cold eyes, and a head of thick white hair. He was not given to sociability but merely came up to me and said, "Brent? Swartz. Let's go to the manager."

We went to the firsr bungalow which had the "manager" sign in front of it. The lieutenant explained why we were there and the elderly man seemed shocked that anything irregular was going on in his respectable place. However, he did volunteer the information that Franklin's parents both worked and that they were seldom home. He took us to the back bungalow and opened the front door with his master key.

Lieutenant Swartz stepped inside. "Okay, everybody out here," he shouted.

There was absolute silence. We all moved into the place. There was nobody there.

"Smart kids," said the lieutenant. "They beat it."

I stood aside while the policemen made a thorough search, and finally, Swartz came up to me. He held out a stub of a cigarette. "But they're never as smart as they think they are," he said coldly. "This was in the sink in the bathroom."

"Marijuana?" I asked.

He nodded. "Thanks for calling, Brent. If we had co-operation from you school people all the time, we might be able to put an end to this dope peddling among our teenagers."

"Peddling? You mean you think Franklin is—"

"We've had our eyes on him for a long time. We think he's the contact for the teenage element around here for a pretty big dope ring that's operating out of the Tiajuana base."

I nodded.

"We haven't been able to nail Franklin with the goods, so far. He's a clever boy."

"Yes," I agreed, with a terrible sadness in my heart. "He is a very clever boy."

"I'm surprised he even let you in the door tonight," he sighed. "He must have really been on it."

I asked, "What's the answer to our juvenile problem, Lieutenant?"

He smiled a little crookedly. "Well, I don't know what all the answers are, Mr. Brent, but I think you've just helped give us one of them."

The next day, I was amazed to find that the news of what had happened had gone through the school like a whirlwind. The rumble was everywhere, and Roger Gates' attitude was typical.

"I hear you broke up a nice little jig when the cats were really jivin' last night, Teach," he grinned, hurry-ing into class. "And they say you got so scared when this chick comes up to you that you ran as fast as you could. You a man or ain't you, Mr. Brent?"

"Roger, sit down," I frowned, "and I don't want to hear any more of this kind of talk, understand?"

The boy went to his seat and looked at me with a sly, wicked smile. I'd received much the same sort of smile from my students all day.

The class had hardly begun when I received a note from Mr. Towers to come to his office immediately. I had expected it, sooner or later. Again I asked Miss Joseph to pinch-hit for me. When I went into the Principal's office, I saw that Lieutenant Swartz was there.

He nodded pleasantly. "Good afternoon, Mr. Brent."

"Pull up a chair, Brent," Towers said coldly. "Lieutenant Swartz was just telling me the story of your . . . er . . . exploits last night."

I sat down, and the lieutenant said, "You did us a real service. We planted a detail to watch Franklin Williams' home. He came in about four in the morning, and we confiscated marijuana from his person and from his car."

"What happened?" I asked anxiously.

"He was so lit he didn't even know what was going on. It didn't take much pressure to get him to tell us all he knew about the ring he was working for. Also, he gave us the names of the other kids who were there when you arrived. We've booked them all. They're in Juvenile."

I felt a sinking feeling within me. "What happens to these kids when they're caught, Lieutenant?"

"The juvenile addicts?" He shrugged. "I don't know, that's not my job. But I sure as hell know what happens to them if they're not caught. While it's claimed that marijuana is not addictive, what it *leads* to is addictive, and it leads to cocaine and heroin. I don't know how true it is but somebody said once that there are only seven or eight people in the world who have ever thrown their addiction to heroin—and they're not dead yet!"

Smiling in a cadaverous way, Mr. Towers asked, "Do you think this will get into the papers, Lieutenant? I mean, with a teacher's being involved . . . well . . . you understand . . . the bad publicity. . . ."

The lieutenant looked at the Principal and his face hardened as I had never seen anyone's harden before. "To be blunt, Mr. Towers, if the educational big-wigs were less concerned about bad publicity and more concerned about our problems with juvenile delinquency, there wouldn't be so much juvenile delinquency."

Towers' face flushed pink. I had an urge to applaud Lieutenant Swartz. Rising, he said, "Well, thanks again, Mr. Brent. You've got a tough job. This is one of the worst areas, and this school is majority delinquent. It took a lot of guts to pull the trigger on those kids last night."

"Guts?" I asked, confused. "I never even thought about that. It was something that simply had to be done."

He smiled. "You must not have been teaching here very long."

"Well, no . . ."

"Where there's a juvenile delinquent, there is always a pal. Some kid who wouldn't give a second thought to shoving a knife in your ribs if you cross his buddy."

Mr. Towers stood angrily. "I think that's going a little far, Lieutenant. . . ."

"You think so?" Laughing without humor, Lieutenant Swartz moved toward the door, then turning back, he said grimly, "Nevertheless, Mr. Brent, I'd advise that for awhile you'd better stay out of dark alleys."

The lieutenant left. I looked at Mr. Towers. "Is that all, sir?"

He nodded heavily. "I'm sorry you got involved with that fracas last night, Brent. It's not a good policy for teachers to be running around playing detective."

"I certainly didn't mean to—"

"It seems as if you never *mean* to do anything which causes trouble, Mr. Brent," he said meaningfully. "I wonder why it is you always do?"

9

The next morning, I found a note in my office box informing me that Mrs. Walter Blackwell wished to have a conference with me. She would come to my classroom at the end of the school day.

George Washington met me. He had an ugly swelling on his left forehead and a minor cut in the middle of his eyebrows. Before I could question him, he asked, "Did you hear about the rumble, with the Chains having a showdown with the Hoods in Adams Park last night?"

"Is that what happened to your face?" I asked him.

"Oh, no," he grinned. "That was just a little personal matter."

"Why did the Chains and the Hoods have a showdown?" I asked.

"The Negro Chains wanta mix with the Mexican chick beans, but the Hoods—they're the Mexican studs—they wanta save those Mexican chick beans all for themselves."

The bell rang and George went to his post by the door. The whole day progressed like an abstract painting by a mad monkey. Black blotches of hate exploded in angry threats; and then there were bright splashes of red when the dabs of desire to learn were fired . . . but these soon faded into dingy pink. Blue was how I felt, and grey was the smog all around me. The painting didn't make much sense . . . the colors simply merged and mixed in fantasy fade-ins and fade-outs, accompanied by the bored tapping of pencils, the stampeding of feet, the noise.

Mrs. Blackwell appeared promptly after school. She was a tall, stately woman with a grim jaw and hard, flat eyes. "I'm Mrs. Walter Blackwell, Marion's mother," she stated in a voice as hard and flat as her eyes.

"Please sit down." I got her a chair.

"I'll get right to the point, Mr. Brent," she began. "My daughter tells me you showed racial prejudice against Angelina Childers."

"I am not a race-prejudiced person, Mrs. Blackwell."

She allowed me a small smile. "Of course, you'd say that, Mr. Brent. All white people do. But as we people know, actions speak louder than words. Your actions regarding Angelina the other day were definitely prejudiced."

"Mrs. Blackwell, the situation is misunderstood. There was no relation at all between what Angelina did and what Ophelia Hernandez did."

"It seems to me, Mr. Brent, that the situations are completely related. It seems to me that the only thing that is different is the color!"

I felt my anger rising. "Mrs. Blackwell, did Marion tell you the reason I sent Angelina to the Principal? Did she tell you what she said in class?"

"I can't see that makes any—"

"Don't you think you people should be more concerned with the filthy language your children constantly use than with bickering over color discrimination?"

Her hard jaw set even harder. "We are not bickering, Mr. Brent. We have gone beyond the bickering stage." Her simple statements somehow seemed to contain an ominous threat.

"Let me try to explain my actions the other day, Mrs. Blackwell," I sighed.

She stared stonily at me while I pointed out my reasons for sending Angelina to the Principal and not sending Ophelia. "So you see," I ended quietly, "the difference in the coloring of the two girls had nothing whatsoever to do with it."

She rose stiffly. "You've simply been trying to worm your way around the obvious truth, Mr. Brent. But I've been fighting racial prejudice too long not to recognize it when I see it. And you, like all the others, are going to have to pay for it." She walked to the door, then turning, gave what was obviously the mature original of Marion's studied threat. "You just wait. You'll see."

Wondering wearily how she would arrive at what she felt would be a fair price for me to pay, I began gathering my papers together. The question haunted me through Johnny Dillon's half hour and as I was driving home. The more I thought about it, the more I felt I should go to Angelina's mother and try to explain my actions. Mrs. Blackwell could hardly cause trouble for me without the backing of Mrs. Childers, whose daughter I had supposedly discriminated against. I only hoped she wasn't the deep freezer the other woman was and that I could reach some semblance of understanding with her.

After an early dinner, I drove to Angelina's address. It was in one of the formerly elegant sections of the city, now delapidated and time-worn. In a two-story frame building, I hunted for the Childers' apartment. As I went up the steps to the second floor, I heard a sudden sound of fast running, and a woman's voice cried out, "You gimme that check, you goddam bastard!"

A door was flung open and a Negro man dashed into the hall, holding what looked like a check high over his head. A red-haired Negro woman whizzed close at his heels, shrieking, "You ain't gonna spend another paycheck on booze! Now you give it to me!" The woman was clad only in a blue bra and blue panties.

Angelina came flying out the door. When she saw me, she stopped short and screamed. The man raced on into another door, slamming it behind him, but the woman turned sharply toward me. For an instant, she froze, then a slow smile crept over her face and she came in my direction.

" 'Scuse my appearance," she giggled. "We was just playin' a little game." She glanced back at Angelina, then got up on her tiptoes and whispered softly into my ear. "You must be the gentleman Willie Mae told me she was gonna send over. You come right on in and I'll get rid of the kid right directly."

Before I could utter a word, she pulled me down the hall, bubbling, "You want the reg'lar dancin' lessons or the special offer?"

As we walked past the still stunned Angelina into the room, the girl blurted, "Ma! That's Mr. Brent! My schoolteacher!"

The woman jumped back as if she'd been stung by a bee. "Oh, my God!" With a gasp, she darted into the next room.

Angelina came slowly inside, staring at me with both fear and hate. "What you doin' here?" she asked huskily.

"I came to talk with your mother."

"What about? What business you got with her?"

Mrs. Childers fluttered back in. She had covered her body with a chenille robe. "Well, Mr. Brent, this is indeed a surprise! To what do we owe such an honor as your visit, sir?" She smiled nervously.

"I want to talk to you about a little problem, if you don't mind, Mrs. Childers."

"Well, please do sit down." She turned to the girl. "Angelina, honey, suppose you go in the kitchen and make Mr. Brent and me a drink. The bottle's back of the trashcan under the sink. But don't you tell Daddy, now, you hear?"

Angelina huffily went out of the room. "And go easy on the water, honey," her mother called after her. Then hastily lighting a cigarette, she said, "As a matter of fact, Mr. Brent, it ran across my mind to want to talk to you. Sadie Blackwell called me up. She's a real upstanding citizen in the community, you know, and she was awful mad."

"I know. She visited me this afternoon. The reason I'm here is to give you an explanation of what happened—the truthful one."

She glanced toward the kitchen. "Angelina, hurry up!"

A man's angry voice rose from beyond the wall. Mrs. Childers' eyes flashed angrily. "That no good— Now he's over there tellin' tales about me to his old lady! You don't know what it's like bein' married to a no-good bum who boozes off every paycheck he's sober enough to get. And every time I try doin' somethin' about it, he runs wailin' and cryin' to his old lady. She's as much a booze-hound as he is!"

I said, "Mrs. Childers, about what happened at school the other day—"

"Angelina!!"

The girl came in with two glasses, gave one to me, and one to her mother. Mrs. Childers asked, "Did you put the bottle back?"

"Yeah," Angelina grunted.

"Okay, but remember . . . don't you tell your Daddy now."

Angelina left the room. Mrs. Childers took a long drink of the iceless liquid. I took a half sip, and shuddered at the strong taste of raw bourbon. Putting it aside, I began a detailed explanation of my actions toward Angelina and Ophelia. The woman listened with childlike fascination.

By the time I'd finished, she was through with her drink. She drained a last, elusive drop and, clucking her tongue, said sadly, "I just can't imagine Angelina using language like that, Mr. Brent. Why, you just don't know how careful I've been bringin' that girl up. It must be them other kids she goes around with, that's what. You know how bad talk rubs off."

"Well, I just hope you understand that I did not show discrimination against your daughter, Mrs. Childers. I try to treat all my students justly."

"I understand, Mr. Brent," she nodded, "I surely do! I sure hope we can get it all straightened out at that Home and School meetin'."

"What Home and School meeting?" I asked in surprise.

"Why, that's what Sadie Blackwell called up about. She said she was gonna bring the whole thing up at the Home and School meetin'."

I sighed, rising. "I see. . . . Well, I'll be running along. I'm sorry I bothered you."

"But you ain't hardly touched your drink yet!"

"Thanks but I have a lot of papers to correct when I get home."

Picking up my drink and sipping it, she followed me to the door. "Mr. Brent, you're a very nice, attractive gentleman," she said, smiling sweetly up at me. "Would you be interested in takin' dancin' lessons?"

10

"As President of the Home and School Association," Mrs. Blackwell announced, "I wish to call our meeting to order. First, let us all stand and take the pledge of allegiance to our flag."

After the pledge had been taken, the secretary read the minutes of the last meeting and the treasurer gave the financial report. Then Mrs. Blackwell bestowed an honorary life membership on Mr. Towers who smilingly accepted and suggested a potluck dinner to celebrate, at his expense. The suggestion was met with warm approval.

The hard, flat eyes gazed at me a moment, then Mrs. Blackwell said, "Tonight, we have a serious problem which the Home and School Public Relations Committee has decided should be brought to your attention, for the benefit of teacher, parent and student. We believe it establishes a closer bond between all of us if we bring controversy out in the open instead of confining it to unkind gossip. Specifically, I am referring to an instance where a parent and a student felt that a teacher showed discrimination in his treatment of a discipline problem. The parent is Mrs. Josephine Childers, who has discussed this with the teacher, Mr. Brent. She received no satisfaction whatsoever."

I glanced in surprise at Mrs. Childers. Her expression revealed nothing more than a touch of envy as she stared longingly at Mrs. Blackwell's shoes which were of a gaily flowered print, boasted extremely high heels, and had small clusters of rhinestones on the toes.

"We have decided to bring this unfortunate situation before this meeting," Mrs. Blackwell was saying, "discuss it like mature adults with charity and understanding, and perhaps restore harmony in our home and school relations. But even more important, we hope that we might set a precedent for the future that will eliminate needless strife."

She then called upon Angelina. Rising eagerly, the girl walked confidently upon the stage and stood before the microphone. She was wearing a simple little-girl dress with a high collar and long sleeves—the opposite extreme from the skin-tight skirts and revealing sweaters and blouses she usually wore. And there was only a trace of color on her lips which were usualy pasted thick with crimson. I couldn't help but admire Mrs. Blackwell's efficiency.

"Now, Angelina, please tell us exactly what happened. We want just the facts, dear, not how you feel about them."

"Should I use the real words?" Angelina whispered uncertainly but the sentence came over the microphone and a there was a smattering of laughter through the audience.

"Just use the letter the word begins with, dear," Mrs. Blackwell said, smiling, and I knew that even this was a planned incident.

Angelina told her story in a soft, sweet voice, and with a lack of hesitation which showed thorough rehearsal. "Well, Mr. Brent lost his temper, I guess, over something I did—I don't know what it was—and he threatened to punish me. I guess I lost my temper, too, at his being unfair, and I blurted without thinking, 'F you.' I reckon I deserved it, but he dragged me down to the Principal's office."

Mrs. Blackwell interrupted with a kind and understanding smile. "There is no doubt that you deserved to go to the Principal for using such vulgarity, Angelina, dear. But go on. Tell us what happened in class later, after you'd come back from the Principal who had given you a just talking-to."

"Well, later on, Ophelia Hernandez lost her temper, too. She shouted out the same word, F, that I did. Mr. Brent did not send her to the Principal, the way he did me. He let her off, and—and—" Angelina deliberately faltered, as if she could no longer control her emotions and was going to cry.

"We understand, dear," Mrs. Blackwell said in a kindly voice. "You may return to your seat."

Ophelia was then called upon to come to the stage. The poor girl looked as tense and frightened as a cowed puppy.

"Ophelia, you have just heard Angelina's report of what happened," said Mrs. Blackwell. "Was everything she said true?"

"Yes, ma'am," the girl nodded meekly.

"You used the same vulgar word she used?"

"Yes, ma'am."

"And you were not sent to the Principal the way she was?"

"No, ma'am."

"What was your punishment for using the same word Angelina used, Ophelia?"

"Well, he—Mr. Brent, he gave me an extra job of homework to do."

Mrs. Blackwell scowled. "An extra bit of homework —that was your punishment?"

"Yes, ma'am."

"Very well, Ophelia, that will be all."

As the girl hurried back to her seat, the audience murmured with disapproval, and angry glances were shot in my direction. Mrs. Blackwell said, "You have heard from the two girls what happened. Now, Mrs. Childers has asked for permission to tell you how she feels about it."

Mrs. Childers walked on stage. She was wearing a conservative tweed suit, and a plain, full hat over her bright red hair. She spoke softly, in the same well-rehearsed manner as Angelina. "It hurts me deeply even to talk about this ugly incident. I wouldn't make an issue of it for myself. I've been pained by racial prejudice so many times, I can take it in my stride. But I won't let them hurt my daughter and get by with it!"

There was a smattering of applause. She went on. "Mr. Brent came to see me. I guess he was afraid his actions would boomerang and he would have to pay for what he'd done. He'd admitted he had punished the girls differently for saying the same word but that the punishment had nothing to do with color. He said the circumstances were different in each case. I told him that it seemed to me that the only difference in the circumstances was the color of the differences! The Negro girl has the right to be treated just as kindly as the Mexican girl!"

"Thank you, Mrs. Childers," nodded Mrs. Blackwell.

The audience applauded as the woman returned to her seat. I was called upon and the applause turned into an angry muttering. I walked up to the microphone and looked out into the audience. The bright house lights made it difficult to see beyond the first two rows but in my limited view, I met unfriendly eyes and knew I must carefully weigh my words.

"Good-evening, parents and teachers," I began. "It gives me pleasure to see so many of you are out tonight for it shows you take an active interest in the education of our children. I appreciate the just manner in which this problem has been brought forth and for the privilege of speaking in my own behalf."

Mrs. Blackwell spoke up. "Mr. Brent, would you please tell us *your* version of the story all the others have told us."

I took a deep breath and plunged. "As I'm sure you all realize by now, during class, Angelina Childers used a foul word. Later, during the same class, Ophelia Hernandez used the same word. I sent Angelina to the Principal for correction. I gave Ophelia an extra homework assignment. As far as these previously stated facts go, they are correct. However, my reason for exacting punishment as I did has not been stated with truth. I am sorry to say that Angelina constantly uses filthy language. I had never heard Ophelia use a foul word before. And in this particular instance, Angelina said the word with no outward provocation whatsoever. She said it deliberately, knowing full well what she was saying. I dealt with her offense accordingly.

"On the other hand, the circumstance under which Ophelia used the foul word was entirely provoked. The boy who sits behind her in class kicked her viciously. In an unconscious knee-flex reaction to pain, she cried out a phrase using the word. The fact that she used this phrase stemmed from two things. She was familiar with it and it lay dormant in her subconscious vocabulary. What brought it to uncontrolled classroom use was the sudden, unexpected shock of the pain brought upon her by another student. 'The quality of mercy is not strained,' as Shakespeare said. But I would have been straining it a great deal if I had meted out the same punishment to Ophelia as I did to Angelina. I did what—"

"Mr. Brent," Mrs. Blackwell interrupted coldly. "There is also the phrase from an operetta song—'Let the punishment fit the crime.' Don't you think that if two crimes are identical, the two methods of punishment should be identical, also? Despite any unprofessional analyzation of the so-called character of the criminals?"

A flame of anger rose through me. "I don't deal with criminals, Mrs. Blackwell! I deal with children! My job is to educate these children and to deal with each one individually and fairly. I am not race-prejudiced. If I were, I would hardly be teaching in a school which is ninety per cent Negro!"

"This is your first year of teaching, Mr. Brent. Perhaps you had no other choice." Glancing at her watch, she added quickly, "Time is running short. Thank you, Mr. Brent."

The place broke into animated conversation as I returned to my seat. Mrs. Blackwell allowed a few moments for it, then called them to order. She held up a mimeographed sheet of paper. "The ushers will now pass these out among you and you will please check number one, which states that you think Mr. Brent acted without discrimination against Angelina Childers, or number two, which says you believe he did discriminate against her. I know you all want to do the fair thing, and I'm sure we all appreciate the fine manner in which Mr. Brent presented his arguments on his own behalf. Let us be charitable in our judgment for we are not here to condemn Mr. Brent for the racial prejudice he claims not to have but which he may have used unintentionally. We are here to take a stand for our children's rights. We are here to insist that in the future, all teachers will know and treat our children as we would have them treated—with equality and justice for all!"

There was thunderous applause. And I knew, with a

sinking certainty, that Mrs. Blackwell's clever histrionics had much more weight than my explanation of the truth. I was right. When the votes were taken and tabulated by a machine, it was found that the great majority believed I had discriminated against Angelina. The countdown was over, and I had lost the fight.

11

Thanksgiving vacation arrived and so did my mother, who planned to stay with my sister, Helen, for the holidays. I had not gone into great detail concerning my problems at school either in my letters to Mother or in my telephone conversations with Helen, but as I looked at my reflection in the Mirror Thanksgiving morning, I thought, *therein lies the truth of the tale*. I looked cadaverous. Brain-wise, I felt just about as alert.

I drove over to Helen's apartment which was in the Crenshaw area. It was small but cheerfully and tastefully furnished, and only fifteen minutes from the beach. Like so many people born and brought up in the midwest, Helen was a sun-and-sea worshiper. And like so many people who are mothers, mine greeted me at the door with tears born of happiness to see me. "Surprised I made the long trip to California?" she smiled.

I nodded, hugging her to me. Mother was a pretty woman, but years of hard work and worry and battling against defeat had imprinted a permanent expression of weariness upon her face. Each time I saw her after any lengthy period, I always felt a touch of remorse that I hadn't taken the opportunities which would have allowed me to make her existence easier and more pleasurable. If I had accepted the partnership my grandfather had offered in his restaurant—if I had taken the offer of an uncle to put me through business college—If! If! I'd spent three years in college preparing myself for ministerial work, then I had changed my mind and switched to teaching. And where was I now? Was there to be still another switch in vocation ahead of me at the end of the school year? Where was it leading to? Where was I going?

"You look tired, Son."

"I am, Mother."

"You must be working hard."

"Pretty hard."

She smiled the particular smile which I think is reserved for mothers who remember the babies their sons and daughters grew from. "You always worked hard, Bob. I'll never forget how you used to do odd jobs for ten cents an hour when you were just a little boy. . . ."

"Hi, stranger!" Helen came into the room, looking as beautiful as always, a frilly apron tied around her waist.

"The other guests will be arriving in about half an hour. I wanted you to come early so you and Mother could have a nice little chat."

"Something sure smells good," I smiled.

She looked at me critically. "You look as if you could do with a good meal. How is it going?"

"Okay," I shrugged.

She nodded knowingly. "Admit it. Aren't you sorry you didn't listen to me and have your assignment changed to a white school?"

"No, I'm not sorry," I said. "It's rough but I think I'll make it."

"Good luck. I hope you do. Maybe when you beat your head up against a stone wall, the wall will crumble instead of your head."

"We'll see."

"Bob was always stubborn," Mother sighed, settling into the corner of the couch. "Sometimes I think there's nothing he can't do if he makes up his mind."

Helen smiled. "Well, you two excuse me. I have to go baste the turkey and look at the yams."

I sat beside Mother. "How are things going at home?" I asked.

She took a tired breath. "Home isn't what it used to be, Son. Remember I wrote you about the city wanting to buy our whole block to build a Negro grammar school?"

"Yes."

"Well, all the Negroes around me sold. The price they offered wasn't bad . . . but it wasn't good. Not good compared to what your father and I paid for our place."

"What did you decide to do?"

"I told them day before yesterday. I'm not selling."

"But your property is right in the middle of the block!"

"I know. I told them they can tear down the other houses and build their school and have their school grounds but I'm staying! I'll just build a fence around the property, that's all."

"Don't you think you should give in, Mother?" I asked soberly. "You can't go on forever fighting—"

"Somebody's got to fight, Bob. There have to be some white people in this country who will stand up for their rights the way the Negroes are battling for what they think are theirs! Why, in some cities they don't even want to build their own schools in their own neighborhoods. They want to take their bastard babies by the busload to the finest white schools in town! They don't care if the poor white people can't get on the bus, they just want to go themselves because they want to mingle and breed with the whites! But God didn't intend it that way, else He'd have made everybody one color. Black is black and white is white, Son, and never the twain shall meet!"

"There has to be a meeting of minds somewhere, Mother," I began, "or else—"

Coming into the room with a plate of hors d'oeuvres, Helen interrupted. "You can't solve the Negro problem. Even a Civil War couldn't solve it. And it will never be solved as long as the Negro goes on thinking that the white world owes him a living. He is demanding rights which he is not willing to earn. He wants jobs which he isn't capable of handling."

"That's where education comes in, Helen," I said. "That's why I—"

"Education? How can you hope to educate a bunch of young savages who hate your guts just because you're white? I read in the paper where one leader claimed he had three hundred thousand Negroes who will mob, rob, steal or kill to get what they want, and if that didn't work, he said, then the Muslims would take over! Does that sound like a civilized man who wants to function in a democratic society and have his children educated properly or does it sound like a violent threat from a heathen savage?"

"There are a lot of Negroes who don't feel that way, I'm sure," I said. "In every group, you'll find rabble-rousers."

"Hitler was a rabble-rouser," Helen countered, "and look at the devastation he caused! Whether you like to admit it or not, Bob, the Negroes in this country have become a menace to decent society! They want to set us back in civilization a hundred years—"

The door chimes sounded as other guests began to arrive, ending the conversation. I was glad. I had to live with the Negro problem every day. I at least wanted to spend Thanksgiving forgetting about it.

But one cannot forget about what one lives with. Helen's guests were intelligent, stimulating people. Naturally, the Negro question arose in conversation. The semantics of equality were discussed. Segregation was debated. Being a teacher in a majority Negro school, I was asked many questions—to most of which I did not have the answers.

My thinking was still stimulated as I drove home that evening. I remembered what one woman had said. "This is not an equal world we live in. Children are not born equal. They don't have equal physical facilities or mental capabilities. And despite the great social fallacy, people do not have equal opportunities."

But they should have equal opportunities, I thought. Whether children are born in Boyle Heights or Beverly Hills, whether their parents are collecting dividends or unemployment insurance, every child on God's earth should be given equal opportunity to make something good of his life, to contribute to society in any way he knows how, to become outstanding in whatever field he so chooses.

And yet, where was the inspiration that would lead a child into doing this? Society preaches conformity. Educational policies dictate 'life-adjustment.' Teach the children to adjust to life the way it is. But wasn't this policy only encouraging an attitude of defeatism, a humble acceptance of one's lot in life? Wasn't this a true crushing of any dormant spirit which might lie within a person to forge upward and onward to a better life, a better world?

Somewhere, I thought, there had to be a key. Granted, it is not an equal world we live in. Nothing is equal and everything is comparative. Could the key to the problem lie not in the fallacy of equality but how we, as individuals, cope with inequality? How we cope with a life with inequal opportunities? Wasn't it up to the individual alone to go forward through intelligence, creativity, self-influence?

But again, the question arose. Where was the stimulation for the child to do this? Where was a child taught that if he was truly "captain of his soul," he would certainly be "master of his fate"?

If a child was lucky, he might be taught this in the

home. But he certainly should be taught it in the school! I decided to give my students a lecture on self-influence. I would tell them not to be influenced by the world outside but by their own inner cravings for individual achievement. No matter what their color or their background, if they wanted to, they could forge upward and onward to a better life, a better world!

12

It was difficult getting the high holiday spirits to subside, but eventually the old routine of minor mayhem was again established. My lecture on self-influence met with minimum success. I was able to reach some of the more sober, thinking students but with the majority, it was the old couldn't-care-less reaction. It was par for the course.

I conducted a survey to see which television shows were the most popular. This assignment met with noisy enthusiasm. The classes buzzed with titles, *Untouchables, Hitchcock, Shock,* etc. One child informed his class in general that he'd seen the movie *Frankenstein* seventeen times.

And then came my Special class. Captain Smith came crawling in with Ruby Burns just behind him. She leaned down and goosed him, hard.

The Captain jumped up, screaming, "Radiation, you no-count coon! You're so cheap you couldn't buy you a down payment on a piece of bubble gum!"

Ruby shouted back, "You're so cheap, you take your toilet paper to the laundry!"

"Don't chop on me, Radiation!" The Captain lunged for the girl who laughingly ducked and ran to her seat.

"Captain Smith, get to your seat at once," I ordered, "and no more of this squabbling from either of you."

The Captain fell on all fours again, and muttering angrily to himself, headed for the Yellow Pages.

When the class was seated and quiet, I said, "Today, I want you to make a list of your favorite television shows. Then we'll have a discussion about television, its proper use, and its misuse."

"I like them neat murder shows," Billy Parrish said loudly.

"Raise your hand before you speak, please, Billy."

Immediately, Billy's hand went up.

"Yes, Billy?"

"I like them neat murder shows," he repeated with heavy sarcasm.

I said, "Take out your paper and pencils, class, and begin the assignment."

They began writing. There was the same enthusiasm which the other classes had shown but louder comparisons of opinion.

"What you writin', Radiation?" Captain Smith asked.

"None of your damn business," the girl whispered harshly, "and if you ever call me Radiation again, I'll take a hacksaw and cut off your you-know-what!"

Captain Smith yelled, "Teach, did you hear that girl, did you?"

"Quiet down, both of you," I said firmly.

When the papers were passed in, I gave the class a reading assignment and I began reading what they had written. Captain Smith listed *Felix the Cat* as his favorite show. Roger Gates preferred *The Untouchables,* as did the majority of students. Geraldine like the soap operas which she watched when she stayed home sick. Angelina was "just crazy" about *Divorce Court.* Marion Blackwell wrote that her favorite program was *Medic,* and that she'd watched all the re-runs.

In not one single instance, unless you want to call *Felix the Cat* funny, did a child mention a comedy show.

When the class was over, I stood outside the room for five minutes and then hurried to the Faculty meeting, scheduled for that afternoon. Again, almost everyone was there ahead of me, munching doughnuts and drinking coffee. I got a cup of coffee and sat down beside Miss Joseph.

"How are things going with you since the big trial?" she asked with a cryptic smile.

"About the same as before," I shrugged.

She nodded. "No matter what happens, good or bad, there is always a day or two of excitement, then everything goes along as it always has."

Principal Towers jangled his little bell and everyone quieted. He began, "Welcome, Faculty. Tonight we have some very important business to discuss. We are happy to have Alice Miller, the district supervisor, with us. She has taken time out from her very busy program to come here today and give us a talk on a matter which vitally concerns each of us."

Everyone applauded and the district supervisor, the woman who had warned me that "we are told" thumbtacks distract, got up. Her blue gabardine suit hung on her like a military uniform. She put on thick reading glasses and held a letter dramatically in front of her.

"First of all, I would like to quote," she said. I thought to myself of course she would have to quote. She continued, " 'We here at the Washington Education Economic Council Committee for Underpaid Teachers wish to report the latest developments in our continuing campaign to get a bill through this session that will open the Federal funds to the teachers.' "

There was a hefty round of applause. Removing her glasses, Miss Miller nodded her approval. "Your professional standing will certainly be enhanced by this bill. This measure guarantees every teacher in this room a substantial raise in salary."

A substanital raise in taxes, too, I thought, as again the teachers applauded. Did they think the Federal Government was a bank where you took money out but did not have to put it in?

Miss Miller raised her right arm in a *Heil Hitler* gesture. "Too long has the teacher been the victim of public indifference! Too long has the stereotyped teacher been the butt of cruel jokes! Too long has the manual laborer had far more economic power than the teacher, and it is not his due!"

More applause.

The district supervisor shook her head sadly. "The teacher's years of costly training have been for nothing, economically speaking. With the race for space a present matter rather than a matter of the future, it is time the teachers rise to true stature and assume their role of leadership and power. The Committee in Washington has been trying to put this bill through for years and it must go through!" She allowed herself a small giggle. "Maybe you'll get that swimming pool or that mink yet, who knows?"

Everyone burst out laughing, again applauding. Miss Miller held up her hand for quiet and went on. "This letter from the Committee emphasizes the absolute importance for each and every teacher to write to Washington, to your representatives, and let them know you want, you demand, Federal aid! I have with me forms which will tell you exactly what has been done and what is going to be done. I shall pass them out. Read them carefully, teachers. And then write to your representative without delay. Remember," she struck a dramatic pose, "there is power in numbers!"

There was more applause as she sat down and Principal Towers rose. "Thank you, Miss Miller," he smiled. "Faculty, I'd like to add one brief word. We mustn't expect the other guy to do our fighting. It's up to each one of us to pull our load. Don't wait! Write to your representative immediately!"

He went on. "The burden which rests upon the shoulders of the teacher today is greater than it has ever been. In this school, more than one-half of the students don't live with their parents. Some of them have been financed by the state from birth and are still being maintained by the state in foster homes. Some of the parents of our children, you may be interested to know, have a bigger income by far than most of our teachers. Why? Because they've gone through long years of college and worked hard? No! Because they have a specialized skill? No! They are paid because they have brought illegitimate children into the world!"

The teachers murmured among themselves. Principal Towers continued, frowning.

"If these people only have one or two children out of wedlock, they don't make much money. But if they turn them out on an automation basis, the profit is great. Some of them make as much as eight hundred dollars a month! They live grandly on money we give in taxes! So I say to you, it is only fair and just that we get Federal government economic aid so we, as educators, can make as much as hard-working unwed mothers! If we don't, perhaps we had better change our occupation!"

The propagate-for-profit theory came comically alive and the teachers enjoyed a hearty laugh. Then the meeting got around to other serious matters, namely the giving of grades. Two other teachers beside myself had had their tires slashed at mid-semester grading. The previous semester, we were warned, sugar had been put in the gas tanks of cars belonging to three teachers, severely damaging the engines.

But as Principal Towers said, "We must remember they're just kids. If we do nothing to irritate them, I'm sure these unfortunate occurrences will diminish."

Another important matter was then brought forth. "We've a little case of robbery," the Principal said simply. "Three lady teachers have had their wallets removed from their purses. My advise to all you women is to keep your purses locked in your file cabinet. Also, four sets of keys were stolen off the front office keyboard. So hang onto your keys and don't let them out of your sight for a moment. Another thing we have to watch is hijacking. The parents of some of our smaller boys have telephoned with complaints. It seems that some of the older, bigger boys are taking the lunches away from the younger ones."

He removed the top from a shoe box on the table before him. "By all means, be on guard against concealed weapons." He took a long, slim blade of gleaming steel from the box. "This straight-razor was taken from one of our boys just last week." He emptied the contents of the box. "And these are a few of the toys we've found our kids playing with during the year." I saw several knives, pieces of glass, long hatpins, chains, several more razors, and a gun.

"This coming Wednesday, we're going to have a Weapons Check. Naturally, it will not be announced. But it will be during your early morning homeroom class. Have the boys empty their trousers' pockets, the girls empty their purses. Make a note of everyone carrying anything which might conceivably be used as a weapon. We'll send someone around to pick up what you've found.

"And now, last but not least, a few words about Christmas. We like the children to enter fully into the spirit of Christmas, and so we have a contest each year in which a specially organized Committee picks the best-dressed homeroom. I'm sure all of you will cooperate with the children in putting forth every effort to win. Miss Stritch will be in charge of the Christmas assembly. The Glee Clubs and the Drama Club will participate, as well as other selected groups from the various classes. If you have any young people in your classes whom you consider particularly talented, please notify Miss Stritch. Also, she wants all English teachers to have the children write stories or poems pertaining to Christmas. Any efforts you find to be on a par of excellence, submit to her, and the child will be given the opportunity to read his material in the assembly. The only rule is that the name of Jesus Christ must not be mentioned in the material. Other than that, they have complete freedom in their choice of Christmas theme."

He glanced at his notes. "I believe that is all the business we need to take up at this—"

Almost involuntarily, I found my hand being raised as a sense of indignant anger rose within me.

Principal Towers focused on me and smiled. "Yes, Mr. Brent? A question?"

I stood. "I would like to know why the name of Jesus Christ must not be mentioned, sir. After all, it is His birthday we are celebrating at Christmas."

The Principal chuckled. "With all due respect to your curiosity and your mental aptitude, Mr. Brent, I'm afraid it has become apparent that you are basically a rabble-rouser."

Some teachers burst into laughter and some quietly sniggered. Some, I sincerely pray in retrospect, saw no humor either in my question or in the Principal's disdainful remark concerning my question.

Pleased with the response, Towers went smilingly

on. "But I shall be happy to give you the ABC's of our reasoning, Mr. Brent. I'm sure you and the rest of the teachers are familiar with the organized efforts to separate church and state. It is now believed to be unconstitutional to force a child to perform religious exercises he might not believe in. To be fair, we must banish the name of Jesus Christ for the sake of those who are not Christians just as we would certainly banish the name of Buddha for the sake of those who are not Buddhists."

He laughed . . . so many followed suit.

"I understand that, Mr. Towers," I said firmly, "and I am quite familiar with modern religious practices in public schools. I know that in schools which still maintain daily devotional periods where the Lord's prayer is recited a child may be excused at his parents' request. But my question has nothing to do with devotional controversy. It has simply to do with the fact that we are celebrating *Christmas*. We are having contests, a ceremonial assembly—plus a two week vacation—because of Jesus Christ! Not to mention His name, when it is His birthday we are celebrating is hypocrisy of the highest order."

"We are not here to argue, Mr. Brent," Towers said with an overemphasized sigh. "The arguing is being done by organizations far more powerful than our humble little handful of teachers. Perhaps, after your Christmas vacation, when you have rested from your strenuous activities, you will see, as I see, that it is not the teacher's lot to be either a rabble-rouser or a rebel. It is the teacher's job to avoid trouble, follow the rules—and forget it. Meeting dismissed."

The following Wednesday morning the voice of the

Boys' Vice-Principal came over the loudspeaker system into the homeroom.

"We are having Weapons Check Day. Students, get to your feet and stand behind your desks."

There was a noisy shuffling as the students stood up.

"Empty your pockets, boys," I said, "and put the contents on your desks."

I moved about the room. When I came to Billy Parrish, I noticed he had failed to empty one of his back pockets.

"Billy, empty all your pockets," I said.

Angrily, he slipped his hand into his back pocket and slammed a jackknife on the desk.

The announcement continued: "Teachers, list the weapons you find along with the student's name. Immediately following homeroom there will be a weapons pickup. All boys found with weapons will report to after-school detention for one week."

"I got another knife at home, Teach," Billy said sarcastically.

"Shut your mouth," exploded George Washington.

I hurriedly listed the names of the boys who had weapons, reminding them to report for after-school detention.

The bell rang. Homeroom was over and the office secretary picked up the small folder containing several long pins, a jagged piece of glass, rusty nails, and Billy's knife.

It was a good thing to have the Weapons Check before Christmas, I thought. At this time of yearly good will it seemed appropriate to do all in our power to prevent violence.

13

Christmas at school seemed as dedicated to tinsel as any big department store putting on the once-a-year splash. There were so many extra activities heaped on the already heavy load of extras, I didn't see how even the most dedicated student could find time for his studies. And they didn't. Work became so bad that, finally, I simply cut it in half, hoping to make up the lost areas when tinsel-time was over.

The decorating of homeroom was frenzied, competition welling into personal and group fighting. My homeroom boys were excitedly creating a cardboard fireplace with Christmas lights around it on the back wall and erecting a chimney to the ceiling.

There was also a great spirit of competition in the writing of Christmas poems and stories. Most of my students followed the " 'Twas The Night Before Christmas" theme and some of the pieces were good enough to submit to Miss Stritch. Most were fair because the children were really trying, for once. Others were unintelligible if not almost illiterate. One was pitiful—Ruby Burns'.

I had allowed none of the pieces to be read aloud until I came to my Special class. As usual, they had to be handled with particular care. I felt sure no submissions to Miss Stritch would come from this group so I would give them at least some vicarious pride in being able to read them before their fellow classmates. Ruby was the first I called upon. She came eagerly to the front of the class and began reading:

> 'Twas the night before Christmas,
> And all through the bomb shelter,
> Not a creature was stirring,
> Not even a robot.
> I looked up! And what do I see?
> A cool space ship was flying at me!
> It hung up above, a door opened below,
> Then I swings on a beam,
> And ups I go like a dream!
> I stares down below,
> Earth's all burned and black,
> Like the inside of a big smoke stack.
> We fly past planets and stars all bright,

And that cool space ship hit Venus
On white Christmas night!

I was touched that the girl nicknamed "Radiation Burns" should choose such a theme, and I praised her for her effort. Most of the others in the class wrote pieces where Santa Claus left literally thousands of wonderful presents for them. In Marion Blackwell's poem, Santa Claus was a Negro and King of the World. In Captain Smith's little story, Santa Claus decreed that never again would he, the Captain, have to go to school, and anyone who defied this law would be struck dead with a bolt of lightning. Billy Parrish began his poem:

'Twas the night before Christmas,
And all through the pad,
Cool Dadde-o was running with the butcher knife,
Like he'd just gone mad.
The black nylons got pushed
Into the fire in the fray!
Lordy, it was a real swingin' Christmas day!
When Dadde-o missed his marijuana smoke—

"That's enough, Billy," I ordered.

"It sure as livin' hell was no joke!" He finished, laughed raucously, and ran to his seat.

At last, the mountainous activities drew to an end. My homeroom won first prize for decoration. The prize was a bunch of silver-painted, plastic roses, which was scotch-taped to the door.

At the Christmas assembly, in the auditorium, there was a huge green tree spread with a multitude of lights and tinsel. On its top was a single, shining, silver star.

I thought how ironic it was that the inspiration for the star was to go unmentioned. The new organ was played for the first time. I recalled with a small chuckle how Roger Gates had contributed the family living room curtains in a three week, marathon, rag-drive to earn money to purchase the organ. Mrs. Gates had frantically raced to school only to leave in a frenzy when she learned that her very good curtains had gone away in a truck as rags. Roger might not be the soul of honesty but he certainly had initiative!

The Glee Clubs sang no songs which mentioned Christ but their voices were magnificent, the music uplifting. Various children recited their poems and stories. The Drama Club performed a play which had all the earmarks of being an original by Miss Stritch—and was. It concerned children who did well in their studies by working very hard and were, therefore, twice-blessed by Santa Claus. There was a brief ballet. The girls wore black tights and had silver antlers on their heads. The boys wore red tights and their heads were adorned with cardboard replicas of Christmas trees. Horribly enough, the ballet was a rude composite of impressionistic dancing to jazz music and a sort of tribal dancing to some weird sounds made by the organist and one of the students who played the drums. I was truthfully surprised they didn't have twisting and the bongos.

It was finally over and I returned to my room to get my things. George Washington and Johnny Dillon came rushing in, each with a brightly wrapped package. I gratefully opened them. They were identical boxes of chocolate-covered cherries. I opened a box and offered them to the boys. Despite watering mouths from chocolate-covered temptation, both refused, wished me happy holidays, and ran out of the room.

That night I drove to International Airport and took a plane for Mexico City. I told myself, relax now. You have two blessed weeks of freedom so leave your problems behind you. Don't worry, don't even think. Spend the Christmas holidays in the attitude of the original conception. Be joyous. Celebrate the birth of Christ with the true spirit of "peace on earth, good will toward men."

But a thought kept nagging at my attempts at relaxation. We were no longer allowed to mention the name of Jesus Christ in the celebration of His birthday. I wondered, was Moscow smiling, God frowning, and Jesus, on His birthday, weeping?

I spent several days sightseeing in Mexico City. The great cities of the world are so close together now that even a schoolteacher, on a limited salary, can enjoy the pleasures of occasional travel. But isn't it strange that with the corners of the globe so close, the human beings upon it can still be so far apart?

I flew to Acapulco for the remainder of the holidays. There, all the problems of my small place in life seemed remote, like a bad dream one knows is bad but that one only recalls vaguely and without gory detail. I walked out to Caleta Beach each day to meet the early morning sun. I swam in the clean clear blue waters, and dozed on the pure white sands. I spoke with people from many countries, and felt a true mental stimulation which I had not felt in months. There were discussions of books, music, the theater, motion pictures . . . debates on politics, economics, world affairs . . . and of course, conversations concerning the Negro problem which was so rapidly becoming predominant in the United States. The attitudes toward this problem were almost as varied as the people who discussed it. One woman said to me, "How fortunate for you to be a part of the big movement! Before too long, the Negro in your country will be on an equal footing with the white, and then you will have a true democracy. And you, as a teacher of Negro children, will have been an important cog in the building of the wheel which is going to turn as your man, Lincoln, wanted it to turn—with liberty and justice for all!"

I made no comment.

One day I swam from the mainland to Roqueta Beach. I talked with a young man who was working as a yacht hand for a couple who were cruising around the world. They were from England. He told me that Great Britain was trying to put a new rule into their immigration laws. Negroes would no longer be allowed to immigrate there because, as he said, "We don't want to get involved in the same mess the United States is in."

While I silently pondered the credibility of his statement, he went on excitedly. "We stopped at this island that had some terribly wacky Negro cult—you should have seen them! They had their hair all done up in a high peak with grease or oil or something, enough to scare the living daylights out of you at noon!"

From what I could gather, he'd been in a bar one night and some of the cultist Negroes had got into a fight with the bartender whom they thought was showing prejudice against them. At the height of the brawl, the theater across the street let out and a group of Negroes from there came over to the bar and joined the melee. The front plate glass window was smashed and a shambles was made of the bar. He said he considered himself lucky to have been one of the few who escaped injury. He was surprised when the police put only the whites in jail even though it had been started by the Black cult. "I guess they were afraid of the cult," he explained.

"Me boss would have gone on along his cruise without me, was I laid up in 'ospital!"

It was all interesting and relaxing and stimulating, and when I took the plane back to Los Angeles, I felt refreshed and invigorated, and ready to tackle even Billy Parrish.

14

I returned to school after vacation with renewed vigor and a list of notes concerning subjects I considered of vital importance to young people. For one thing, I wanted to point out to them the important connection between their school work and their future lives, after they graduated. Most of them didn't seem to realize that school was not an end in itself. They didn't comprehend that it was a preparation for life. If I could get this across to them, make them see it visually with some self-image, perhaps I would have pulled the trigger which would fire them into *wanting* to learn.

In Period One, I told them I was certain all of them wanted to get the best job they could after they graduated from high school.

"What do you see yourselves as doing in the future?" I asked. "Do you picture yourself in a clean, white, starched uniform, a nurse tending the sick? Or a doctor, giving a human being a life he might have lost without you? Do you see yourself as a lawyer, defending the innocent from injustice?"

I told them that professional people such as these were an invaluable part of life and it took a lot of hard work to attain such a status. "But just as valuable to the existence of humanity is the skilled laborer. The electrician, the plumber, the mechanic, the seamstress, the stenographer, the bookkeeper, the telephone operator, the television repairman—all of these are skilled laborers, just to name a few. Without them, life could not go on. Perhaps you see yourself as one of these, as part of a giant machine which is part of the stuff which makes the world go round."

To my relief, all eyes were on me, and they were listening with rapt fascination. I could almost see the images floating through their plastic young minds.

"Now, I want to read to you a portion from an official release from the Labor Department in Washington. It applies to each and every one of you, and the world you will find yourself in after you graduate." I read, " 'The unskilled boy or girl between the ages of eighteen and twenty-five will find himself out of luck in the age of automation. More machines will replace more men, creating a labor pool surplus. New job openings for specialized skills will be available but on a highly competitive basis.' "

I explained in simpler terms what the report meant, and told them how important it was that they become skilled in some job. Their interest was waning but I pressed on, illustrating how competence in school meant competence in work after school.

"We can always go on relief," I heard someone whisper with a giggle.

I ignored the remark and went on, but by the time I'd finished my lecture, hardly anyone was listening. A teacher knows when he is communicating with his students, and I was not communicating. Perhaps Mr. Towers was right, I thought in depression as the class ended and the students milled out of the room. Perhaps I simply did not know how to communicate. Or was it my fault, personally? Could it be the fault of the system which had already taught them to adjust to whatever was handed them—taught them not to accept the challenge of the future?

I continued with the lecture through the day, despite my seeming failure in Period One. If I could make just one of those plastic young minds comprehend the truth then it would be worth facing the blank, daydreaming eyes of the others.

I was wondering whether or not to give the lecture to my Special class when Geraldine came running into the room and blurted, "Teach, Billy Parrish poked at my you-know-what!"

Right behind her, Billy cried, "I never touch that girl!"

"Yes, you did, you no-count coon!"

"You a lyin' bitch—"

"Sit down!" I ordered, slapping the ruler on the desk angrily. "Your behavior is disgusting."

"You call me names and I get the Chains to take care of you," Billy sneered.

"Don't threaten me, Billy," I said sternly.

He moved slowly, menacingly, toward me. "On second thought, I think I'll take care of you myself—right now!"

Evenly, I said, "Go to your seat immediately." My eyes held the hate in his a long moment, then he looked away, and muttering to himself, went to his seat.

By the time the class was seated and quiet, I had decided to give them a watered version of the lecture. "Students," I began, "would you think of going to a second-rate doctor if you were ill? He wouldn't charge you as much as a first-rate doctor, perhaps, but he might not be able to help you. You might die. Undoubtedly, he would excuse himself by saying he had done the best he could, and he would possibly be right. But a first-rate doctor would have been able to do better because his work would be more skilled, he would be more capable—"

Geraldine raised her hand and I gave her permission to speak. "A bad doctor can get into a lot of trouble," she said earnestly. "If he does a lousy job of cuttin' on somebody and they die, he could have more trouble than he knows what to do with cause that stiff could become a ghost and haunt the livin' daylights outta that no-count doctor!"

Billy Parrish snorted disgustedly. "Crazy girl . . ."

"I ain't crazy," Geraldine went on excitedly. "There is ghosts! The dead do come back and I seen it!"

I started to stop her but the class had become so enthralled, I knew I could never gain their attention until she finished her fanciful tale.

She went on in a respectfully hushed tone. "One night I couldn't sleep for thinkin' of my dear departed sweet mama. I was all alone, and then I got hungry, so I got up and went into the kitchen. I opened up the door of the icebox . . . and right there . . . in that old icebox . . . there was my mama! She was just sittin' there and lookin' at me with that sweet smile she always had, and I—"

"Your Ma was stiff all her life," blurted Billy with a coarse laugh, "and she was dead and stiff in the icebox!"

The class burst out laughing. "Livin' drunk stiff and dead frozen stiff," howled Roger Gates.

Geraldine jumped out of her seat. "Don't you dare make fun of my dear departed mama," she shrieked, and lunged for Billy who jumped up and back.

"Geraldine! Stop it this minute!" I shouted above the sudden uproar, moving toward the girl as she began trying to claw at the boy's face.

I separated them and each of them sat huffily in their seats. Then, just as I'd returned to the front of the room, the take-cover siren sounded for the Atom Bomb drill. "Down on your knees," I ordered quickly. "Put your hands over your head, and absolutely no talking!"

As I flicked out the lights, Captain Smith cried, "Is this a real A-bomb bust? Are them Russians gonna bust a bomb right on us?"

"This is just a test drill, Captain," I said. "Now be quiet. It will soon be over."

The students obeyed as they never had before. It seemed as if they were paralyzed into silence. Perhaps it was the talk of ghosts which had instilled some fear and righteousness into them, I thought with amusement.

When the drill was over, I went on with my lecture. I was telling them that if they wanted the best job they could get after school, their training should begin by hard work in school, when Marion Blackwell raised her hand and spoke.

"When the whites won't give a Negro a fair chance at a job, anyway, what's the use of workin' hard? The only jobs a Negro gets a chance at is janitor, and garbage collector, and hod carrier. He gets the left-over jobs, the ones the whites don't want and wouldn't soil their lily-white hands with! Nobody needs any learnin' to pick up garbage!"

"Now, Marion—"

"But that's all going to change," she interrupted forcefully. "The Muslims are gonna change everything. The Muslims are gonna have the lily-whites pickin' up their garbage! You wait. You'll see."

Ignoring her hate-tipped darts, I gave Roger, who had his hand raised permission to speak.

"Teach, the way it seems to me, this whole damn world is gonna be blown to hell and back," he said with excitement. "Them bombs are gonna fly and there ain't gonna be nothin' left of nobody, not even any little bitty pieces. So what's the good of studyin'? Might as well just get your kicks while you still kickin'!"

Ruby said, "Teach, let us all write about the bomb, okay? Let us write stories."

Billy Parrish snickered. "You oughta write a real good story about that swingin' bomb, Radiation, cause you already got an atom bomb face."

Ruby jumped out of her seat, and for the second time during the period, Billy was attacked. "You get your radio-active hands off me, girl," he yelled.

"I'll cut your chicken heart out and roast it on a spit!"

Again, I separated the fighters. Then I decided to give up with my lecture. It was leading to nothing but squabbling and depression. I gave the class a writing assignment. "Write anything you want to," I said wearily. "A story, a poem—anything."

That night, I spent my usual hours correcting papers and notebooks. When I came to the assignment given my Special class, I found I was reading a mass of error and nonsense.

There was Billy's usual filth. There was Marion's usual hatred. Captain Smith had simply drawn a huge X on his paper. Geraldine had written the story of seeing her mother in the icebox. And Ruby had written about the bomb. As with her Christmas poem, it brought a feeling of pity into my heart. She wrote:

> I was going home from school when a terrible noise zoomed through the air. It was the take-cover signal. At first I thought it was just another test. But this was for real. A truck came round with a loud speaker tellin everybody it wasn't no test, it was happenin!
>
> I started runnin home to my bomb shelter as the school didn't have none. My heart was poundin so damn fast it was like it would pop right outta me. I ran by a fence and tripped and fell on a broken bottle. I cut my leg and blood was spurtin out like a flash-flood. I wrapped my leg up to stop the bleedin. Nobody stopped to help me because everybody was runnin around and not knowin what to do, like they'd gone wild.
>
> I went limpin on home. I saw a man who lived by my house get run over with a car. Then I saw my ma and my sister wavin for me at the entrance to the bomb

> shelter. I was almost there! Then I saw a neighbor lady rush up to the door with her baby. Ma pushed her down. She got up. My sister took a stick and hit her over the head. The woman fell down again and just lied there. The baby lied there, too, cryin real hard.
>
> Then all of a sudden the whole sky lit up as it had never lit up before. Ma and my sister hurried into the bomb shelter. The door closed behind them.
>
> I ran up to the door and pounded on it. But nobody opened it up. I just stood there at that bomb shelter door, poundin and poundin and poundin, but they never let me in.

Not only pity for the child whose soul had become maimed because of her scarred face and her nickname filled me, but I felt a kind of horror, unidentifiable and yet complete. The world-annihilation threat had tainted all of us, even the children. And wasn't it true that whether we liked it or not, we had to condone mass murder—for survival? The atom bomb, the hydrogen bomb—the enormity of conscious guilt man must bear for these weapons was staggering. Should I really be so alarmed at the petty hates, the foul words, the fighting of my children when adult society had created a thought pattern of frozen-faced mass murder?

Yes, I thought, I should be alarmed! These children were the adults of tomorrow. The petty fights, foul words, and fighting of today could be the pushing of the panic button that would send the first mass-murder bomb into space tomorrow.

If we could cast out the small hates of today, God willing, they might themselves cast out the big hates of tomorrow.

15

The days passed, some good, some bad, most of them just passable. And then the time I dreaded arrived—semester grading. I had a true battle with myself the night I made out the report cards. It seemed as if I had an angel on one shoulder, a devil on the other. I wanted to be in Principal Towers' good graces. I wanted no trouble from the students, no more slashed tires, no sugar in my gas tank, no indignant accusations.

On the other hand, I had a stanch set of values to maintain. Before I'd begun teaching, I hadn't given much thought to a personal philosophy of education. I had simply assumed that one of the beauties of America was that a gifted person, even with a background of the worst poverty, could, through effort and determination, elevate himself to heights no other nations on the face of the earth dared dream possible in their cramped comprehension of the individual and society. America, with its free social structure, had developed crowning competence in scores of areas. In education, I felt the standard of excellence was just as vital as the free education factor which extended literacy among our people as no other nation had.

The question was, should I stay on the safe side and grade my students according to Mr. Towers' philosophy or should I endanger my standing not only with him but with the students by giving an honest evaluation of their work?

I don't know whether it was the angel or the devil who finally won out but I gave the grades I thought the children deserved. I knew I would get it from both ends, but I would just have to stand up for what I knew to be right and fight it through.

I had beaten my brain so ruggedly and was so weary, I had a troubled sleep and could hardly pull myself out of bed the next morning. A feeling of comedy hit me when I decided to park my car with its very good tires and its very good engine several blocks away from the school, and I laughed to myself. I was pulling the tactics of a soldier going into battle.

"And just hope you're not killed," I thought wryly. I knew I'd be wounded.

Because of my parking precaution, I was two minutes

late. With his icy smile, Mr. Towers put a big check next to my name on the goof sheet. I wondered briefly if he'd see the humor in my reason for tardiness but knew he wouldn't, so I hurried on to my classroom.

George Washington bounded toward me down the hall. It tired me just to witness his vitality. "Today's my big day, Teach," he grinned, taking my briefcase. "Today, I just know I'm gonna get my first A."

I smiled. "Well, I don't know how you've done in the other classes, George, but I'll tell you right now that you're getting an A from me."

"Gee, Teach, that's swell," he grinned happily. "Thanks mucho!"

"Don't thank me. Thank yourself. You've earned it."

The day inched by as no other. In order to avoid mass anger outbursts, I gave each class reading assignments and called the students up individually to give them their report cards. The mean looks, the sneers, the angry retorts, and the accusations of injustice I received in those hours would have been enough to drive away even a saint's sanity.

In my Special class, Angelina looked at her D and muttered, "Just what I expected from somebody who's race-prejudiced!"

Marion Blackwell yelled wildly, "I never got a D in English before in my life! I ain't gonna take this crap from nobody! I'm gonna tell Mr. Towers and you gonna find yourself fired!" She stalked out of the room and I knew there was no use trying to stop her.

When he got his B, Johnny Dillon beamed with such happiness that all my efforts with him were richly rewarded.

Billy Parrish looked at his D and rage contorted his face. "I deserve a C," he said in a kind of animal growl.

"No, Billy," I said. "You deserved exactly what you got because it was what you earned."

"Fuck you," he cried viciously.

I rose quickly. "You're going to the Principal!"

He started backing away from me. "Oh, no, I ain't! But I tell you what I am gonna do. I'm gonna kill you, Mr. Brent!"

"Calm down, Billy—"

"I'm gonna kill you, you hear me? I'm gonna kill you!"

I started toward him and he turned, running from the room. Just then, a student messenger came in with a note from Mr. Towers. He wanted to see me after school, and I was to bring my rollbook. Well, I thought, as the closing bell rang, I had expected to get it from the students and I had. I'd also expected to get it from Towers—and obviously, I was going to.

When I went into the Principal's office, I found the head of the English Department there. Both he and Towers looked at me with cold accusation mingled with contempt. I sat down and there was no dillydallying. The Principal began abruptly:

"Marion Blackwell came to me with a complaint, Mr. Brent. She says you are the first teacher ever to give her a D."

"Perhaps I'm the first teacher to give Marion Blackwell the grade she deserves," I said flatly.

The Principal sighed. "You will undoubtedly have the opportunity to tell that to Mrs. Blackwell when she flies into a flurry—as I'm sure she will."

"Could I look at your rollbook, please, Mr. Brent?" asked Mr. Rickards.

I gave it to him. He began counting rapidly, jotted down totals, and gave the slip of paper to the Principal. Looking at me as if I had just flown in from outer space, he said, "You've given thirty-five D's and seven Failures."

"I gave exactly what the children deserved." I said evenly.

Mr. Towers shook his head slowly from side to side. "Communication . . . that must be the answer . . ."

"Would you care to see the work I gave the D's and F's for?" I asked.

"I don't need to see the work," Mr. Towers said bluntly. "If you were communicating, their work would be up to par."

It was like a broken record. I decided to bring up a matter I considered of equal consequence. "I naturally had trouble with the students who didn't receive the grades they wanted," I said. "But Billy Parrish got so angry, he was almost maniacal. He used a foul word, and then when I threatened to send him to you, Mr. Towers, he threatened to kill me. Actually, he repeated the threat three times, then ran out the door. I think the boy is potentially danger—"

"Send him to Social Adjustment Room tomorrow," said Mr. Towers without concern.

"I think Billy needs something more than a trip to Social Adjustment," I said heatedly. "If that kid isn't curbed, he's going to be in real trouble."

"I'd appreciate it if you'd let me handle my business the way I see fit, Brent," Towers scowled. "These kids talk like that all the time and it doesn't mean a thing. 'Kill' really means simply 'dislike' to them. When they say they're going to kill you, they are really saying they just don't like you!"

I had no answer and the Principal shortly called the interview to a halt but I knew, as I walked from the office, that it was far from being the end of the matter.

When I arrived the next morning, the Principal once again asked me into his office. He sat down heavily. "The office has been deluged with complaints from parents," he said, "not just yesterday afternoon but already this morning."

I said, "Perhaps if the parents would see to it that their children do the work they're supposed to do, they wouldn't get so hot under the collar when their kids don't get good grades."

He sighed. "So now you're blaming it on the parents, Brent."

"No, not completely. I'm sure some of it can be blamed on the carload of activities we have going for the kids. So far this year, we've had a Rag Drive, a Cookie Drive, a Homeroom Attendance Drive, drives for the Red Cross and the Community Chest. Every week there is a Boy Scout and a Girl Scout meeting. There are the Travel Club, the Horticultural Club, the Calypso Club, the Homemaker's Club, the Horizon Club, and the Glee Clubs and Drama Club. The children are also involved in Student Government, in Office Help, in Cafeteria Help. We've had contests for the Girl and the Boy of not only the month but the week! We had a Best Smile contest. There are the boys' tumbling group and the girls' modeling group. There's the—"

His laughter interrupted my frustrated list. "Brent, you're trying to make it sound like a circus."

"That's exactly what it seems like to me, Mr. Towers," I countered, "more like a circus than a school."

"You're simply too inexperienced to realize how important these activities are to kids," he said, not unpleasantly, "so I won't take your remarks as insubordination. Besides all this has nothing to do with the real point. Mrs. Blackwell called about Marion's grade, as I think we both knew she would. She was pretty upset, if you know what I mean."

I recalled the woman only too vividly for comfort and knew very well what he meant. "Actually, I was doing Marion a favor by not failing her," I informed him. "She was right on the borderline."

"Mrs. Blackwell maintains that Marion never gets any homework, so how could she get a good grade?" he asked evenly.

"That's not true. I give much more homework than the other teachers. The kids are always complaining about how much homework I give them."

He shrugged. "Not according to Mrs. Blackwell, and to several of the other mothers who phoned."

"My Lesson Plans show how much homework I give," I said indignantly.

"A Lesson Plan is one thing, Mr. Brent. Following through with the Lesson Plan is something else again. You've got to have proof that you follow through."

"You mean, my word isn't good enough?"

Avoiding answering, he said, "We've got to do everything we can to pacify the parents. I would suggest that you find a better way of giving assignments, possibly even a foolproof way. I've got to have something to show the parents when they come in with a gripe about their kids."

"All right," I said narrowly. "I'll make out an assignment sheet, dated, and have each student sign it as he receives his assignment. That should be proof enough."

He agreed to this tactic and I left the office. I used the few moments before homeroom to make up a mimeographed assignment sheet but I was filled with disgust that such a thing was necessary. What kind of system was it that would have a teacher in hire but refused to accept his word concerning the children?

My chosen topic for the day was: "What benefits do you get from public education?"

Between Period One and Period Two, I read some of the answers written on that very important topic. To list a few:

"We don't get any good out of school. The reason is I don't know."

"I don't like school at all. You can't wear your skirts above your knees and you can't chew gum."

"We can't carry big purses and we can't chew gum. Only good we get out of school is some parties and some dances."

"You like school, Mr. Brent, cause you get paid for coming to school. If they'd pay us for coming to school, we'd like it, too. Do you dig me?"

"I like to cut up in class because I feel more happier. It give you engy and pep. I like to make noise—hit people while they are not looking but I don't mean no harm to no one."

"I like to chew gum, make noise, and throw things. But I'm trying to be good in school so I will gets degree."

And these were the children who expected to get an A or a B in English! Of course, they weren't all of such low quality. George Washington wrote:

"America is a free country and that is why we get free education. If that wasn't so, I might never be able to learn to read and write and be a doctor. I might have to be something lowly and mean. But free public school means I get a chance to better myself."

One girl in Period Two wrote, "Free public school education is what Columbus discovered America for. And I am glad the Negroes were brought here as slaves in the first place. Though I'm glad Mr. Lincoln done freed the slaves. If it wasn't for Mr. Columbus and Mr. Lincoln, I might be living in darkest Africa right this minute and fighting off lions instead of having free public school."

Well, thank God a couple of students pulled through this assignment in great shape, I thought.

There was an assembly that day. As a reward for having done so well in the Rag Drive, the children were shown an old movie. It was called, *The Creature From the Black Lagoon.* The later classes didn't go as well as the early ones. It was difficult for school work to compete with the Creature. But they all wrote their class assignments and no one objected to signing the assignment sheet—until the last class of the day.

"I ain't gonna sign nothin'," Marion Blackwell announced firmly, and instigated a total wave of nonsigning.

"It's Mr. Towers' order, Marion," I said firmly. "He wants proof that all of you receive homework assignments."

"It ain't Mr. Towers' at all," the girl said smugly, "it's you. Mr. Towers, he's on our side but you ain't. You're race-prejudiced and we found out how we can get you fired."

Angelina giggled. "Marion's right. We know how we can get you fired, Mr. Brent!"

"How?" I asked.

Marion laughed. "Miss Malone, the gym teach, she told us that any teacher who cussed could get fired. You cuss, we tell the Principal, and the Principal, he tells the Board of Education—and zoom! You're fired!"

Angelina giggled again. "And we just bet we can get you mad enough to cuss, Mr. Brent!"

"I bet I can get you mad enough to cuss right now, Teach," Bill said loudly, an evil grin spreading across his face. "I bet if I just stood up and said shallow shit, you'd cuss."

He jumped to his feet and shouted, "Shallow shit! Shallow shit!"

It was next to impossible to conceal the rage I felt that moment. I took a deep breath and said, "Billy, I'm taking you to Mr. Towers right now!"

Billy quickly made a slingshot of a rubber band and the next instant I felt a jagged sensation of pain in my left eye.

"God!" I exclaimed.

Now they were all silent.

"You mean Billy Parrish, shooting putty into Mr. Brent's eye," Geraldine Robinson exclaimed.

I opened my left eye. My vision was wavy and blurred.

"Let's go, Billy," I said, walking toward him and holding one hand over my left eye to ease the pain.

He stood motionless, perspiration breaking out on his face, his eyes widening into enormous circles. In a flash his hand shot into his pocket and he brought out a gleaming steel knife. I stopped short, gripped with sudden fear, then quickly I brought all my senses into balance. The vision in my left eye was still blurred.

"Give me that knife, Billy."

His hand which held the small-bladed knife was noticeably trembling and his voice was shaking as he said, "You just try to get it!"

I moved slowly toward him. "Give me that knife!"

He darted toward the front corner of the room. His face was streaming now and he was panting heavily.

"Give me that knife!"

Swiftly, he raised his arm. The knife shot cleanly across the room, just over the heads of the students, and landed quivering in the door between Miss Joseph's room and mine.

"Man, that was a good throw, Billy," Captain Smith shouted gleefully.

Miss Joseph opened the door and looked at the knife.

"Would you cover my class for me?" I asked her.

"Yes," she said softly and I knew she was thankful she hadn't opened that door a second earlier.

I removed the knife and walked with Billy to Mr. Towers' office. He wasn't in. Just then the closing bell rang. I told Billy to report to Mr. Towers the first thing in the morning. He nodded. My vision was still blurred and my eye still pained. I was anxious to go to a doctor.

The next morning I went into Towers' office.

"Brent, I got your note about Billy Parrish along with the knife. I plan to send him to Social Adjustment today. And I heard something happened to your eye."

"A piece of putty shot by Billy Parish from a rubber-band slingshot hit my eye and injured it," I said.

"Exactly where is the injury?" he asked, putting his own hand to his face and feeling near his eye in a motion that indicated he doubted the injury as he could see none.

"It's a nerve injury back of the eyeball," I told him flatly.

"Hmmm—you know I used to play football and I never got injured once."

"Good," I replied.

He nodded. "Now I need the name of your doctor. We must make out a medical report and I guess I'll have to suspend Billy for a couple of days."

I said nothing.

He scowled and said, "You know I've been wondering if you can handle it, Brent."

"You mean you'd threaten to fire me because a student injured me?"

"I don't mean to threaten you," he said, smiling, "I'm merely warning you that things look bad." He frowned, "And it doesn't look good for any of us in the downtown office when a teacher is injured."

"I understand," I nodded, thinking that this was a real red-letter day!

16

It was a red-letter day in more ways than one. The teachers had been given books on Communism the previous day. We had been instructed to review them before our classes. The doctor had advised me to go easy on my eyes and give them all the rest I could for a couple of weeks, so I hadn't had a chance to go over the book. I glanced over it quickly before homeroom and I was not only puzzled, I was startled.

One book stated that the United States and Russia were both democracies, just different kinds. It said that Russia felt her democracy was the superior road to freedom. It failed to say the United States felt its democracy was the best road to freedom.

I glanced through one of the other books. I read: "What then are the prospects for Soviet-American relations? At the worst, the prospect is for either nuclear war or a gradual American capitulation out of fear, dismay and lack of stamina to face up to the challenge which history has put on our national doorstep.

"At the best, the prospect would seem to be for some future accommodation arrived at only through a vigorous and sensitive prosecution of the Cold War. Such an outcome will involve Americans in much effort and sacrifice, it will involve difficult choices, it will entail dangers and uneasiness for many years to come. . . ."

This was what we were to teach our children? It seemed incredible. Then I recalled the words of J. Edgar Hoover: "To dismiss lightly the existence of the subversive threat in the United States is to deliberately commit suicide. In some quarters we are surely doing this."

I felt no doubt about it. The subversive political and economic philosophy which we were asked to teach was not only suicide, it was tantamount to the murder of liberal democracy. It went along with the theory of progressive education. Don't teach the children their own history. Don't instil in them a sense of tradition. Because if you don't, their pliable young minds will be vulnerable enough to accept any and all un-American, one-world propaganda handed to them without question.

I did not read from the books on Communism in my classes that day.

Then, just before the closing bell, Miss Miller, the district supervisor, stalked in. She wore the same military-type blue gabardine suit and the same troubled expression I'd seen her wearing last. Immediately, her beady eyes saw every detail in the room including, I'm certain, the gum-filled mouths of several students. She sat stiffly in the back of the room until the students left, then she came—or should I say charged?—up to me.

"How is it going, Mr. Brent?" she asked solemnly.

"I'm trying," I said, "but I still have my problems."

"So I hear." Her voice took on an ominous overtone. "May I see your Lesson Plans?"

I gave them to her. She studied them quickly, then with a deep scowl, said, "I don't see three activities listed for each class period."

I fought a sigh of utter weariness and said, "There is nothing I'd like more than to see these kids perform three activities during their class period, Miss Miller, but it seems to be an impossibility for them. I believe it is better for them to perform one activity thoroughly and well than to attempt to have them do three in a smattered, hurried fashion."

Coldly, she replied, "If you were performing your job as a teacher in as thorough a manner as you should, I'm certain the children could easily perform three activities—well. As you know, the taxpayers in California voted to let Sacramento select the textbooks. That is now the law. To make California tops in teacher assistance, we have put out the Study Guide Outlines. Years and years of work and thousands of dollars have gone into this. You are demanded to select at least three activities from the guide per day. In this way, the state educationalists can keep track of the teacher's work in the classroom."

She spoke as if she were reciting a fairy tale to a child and I knew better than to voice my opinion. But I did. "Frankly, Miss Miller, I feel the voters made a mistake when they gave up their freedom of text selection to the state officials. I think the local administrators, the teachers, and the parents, should have a voice in picking the textbooks their children are going to learn from. I'm sure the Study Guide Outlines have some benefit, but to use them in a blanket fashion as if they were a Bible is wrong. The variances of individuality must be taken into consideration. The people who make up these outlines haven't seen the youngsters I'm working with. They don't know and aren't familiar with the problems of the individual children—with Billy Parrish or Captain Smith or Marion Blackwell. Ordering complete adherence to their outlines is as ridiculous as a doctor prescribing a cure for a patient he has neither seen nor diagnosed."

"Is that all you have to say?" she asked bitingly.

"That's about all," I answered.

"Perhaps you had better do a little less 'saying,' Mr. Brent, and a little more 'doing.' Your views clash with our policy and you are merely one individual while we are many. You should learn to follow orders because, obviously, the majority is right."

"That is not always true, Miss Miller—" I began angrily.

She interrupted. "The best policy to follow is the policy which is in power, Mr. Brent. I'm afraid that I cannot conscientiously give you anything but the lowest of recommendations. Your performance has been both weak and unsatisfactory. Also, you have a rebellious nature." She was smiling—if you can call it that. "I never overlook good points, however," she said. "I see that you followed my instructions concerning your bulletin board. Your pictures are hung evenly. And you are using straight pins. I'm so glad . . . because thumbtacks do distract!"

As I drove home, I felt almost dead. There was so much to think about, so many conclusions yet to be reached. The books on Communism from the Board of Education, the low recommendation from Miss Miller —I even found myself pondering the validity of straight pins versus thumbtacks. And that night, I had to attend the male faculty party, a yearly affair, which was being held at the home of Jack Farrell, one of the music teachers. I didn't really want to go but Miss Joseph had warned, "The stag party is one of Towers' pet activities. If you don't show up, he might not like it. And who knows? Outside of school, he might be a regular guy."

When I arrived at Jack's house most of the other teachers were there along with Mr. Towers, a principal from a neighboring school and some guests from other schools. Obviously, a good time was being had by all.

Towers came toward me through the crowd as if he were plowing down center field. "Good you could come, Brent." He shook my hand vigorously. "This is your first time at one of our little stag parties and I want you to know we're here just to unbend and have ourselves a ball! We leave our professional disagreements outside the door." He winked. "The wife's out so you don't have to watch your language—and the drinks are in the kitchen."

He launched off toward someone else who had just

come in. I got myself something to drink and roamed around. None of the others spoke much more than a formal greeting to me and seemed to be on guard against any more personal contact. I could understand it. My clashes with the Principal were common knowledge. Probably none of them dared incur the dark wrath of Towers by appearing to be a cohort of mine. Perhaps he had left his "professional disagreements" outside the door but he hadn't spread the word around.

I was enjoying the buffet when someone shouted, "Hey, Harry! When are you going to show the movies?" There was a general blast of laughter. Harry Waterfield, the Boys' Counselor, laughed the loudest and said, "Don't worry, boys, you'll get to see your movies! And I've got a new one this year that'll knock you over—bought it in France last summer."

"Well, stop stalling, Harry," Towers boomed happily. "You know how we look forward to your little educational films!"

There was hearty agreement to this. Harry began setting up a screen and a projector. The others hurriedly pushed to the kitchen for last-minute drinks. Finally, everybody was settled. The lights went out. The projector went on. A scenic landscape flickered on the screen and a man's voice announced: "We are about to show you the finest bowls in the world—the Peruvian bowl. Peru has produced some of the most interesting, artistic, and beautiful bowls known to man. For centuries, this art has flourished—"

"Hey, Harry!" someone bellowed. "Are you kidding?"

"Yeah! What kind of junk is this, anyway?"

"Where are the movies?"

There were multiple thunderous objections. Harry

laughed raucously. "But this is an educational movie, guys! You're educators!"

"Screw education!"

"Screw Peruvian bowls! We want the movies!"

A chant started. "We want the movies, we want the movies!"

"Okay, okay," Harry shouted. "You'll get your movies! I just wanted to see if you were paying attention!"

Quickly, he changed reels on the projector, explaining that he'd just wanted to have his little joke. Then the screen lighted up again. To a savage, rhythmic drumbeat, a girl so voluptuous that she was almost bovine undulated into sight. A flowered skirt was tied around her waist and a lei hung about her neck. The film crackled and skipped, fuzzed, and came back into focus. Despite the poor quality, the men howled their approval.

"They got native girls in France, Harry?" someone yelled.

"They got all kinds of girls in France! Like wow!"

Her hips swinging to the beat of the drum, the girl slowly lifted the lei over her head, revealing enormous, red-nippled breasts. The men shrieked, clapping their hands excitedly.

"Cool, man, cool!"

"Jesus, take a look at those titties!"

Someone made lewd sucking sounds.

"Take it off, baby, take it off!"

The girl turned and twisted, accommodatingly slipping out of her skirt. Completely naked, she began performing bumps and grinds, moving slowly toward the camera.

"Come on, baby, come on up close!"

"Come to daddy, sweetheart!"

As the girl slithered down to the ground, her hips still undulating, her breasts still shaking, and spread her legs at wide angles, I looked about the room for Towers. He was sitting on the sofa, a broad smile on his face, nodding his approval. I found the other principal. He was quietly watching the film with interest. Some of the other men seemed to be embarrassed but were nevertheless attentive.

As the camera zoomed in for a huge close-up and the girl began massaging her vagina, the room became uncontrolled bedlam. Fortunately, I was seated in the back. As quietly as I could, I rose and moved to the front door and out. But I think if I'd tripped, fallen, and broken a leg, no one would have noticed me.

Outside, I breathed deeply of the clean chilly air. What kind of faculty party was this? What men individually wanted to do was their own business but to demand the presence of teachers at a perverted display of lewd sexualism and call it a "faculty function" was no less than moral rape! How two school principals could not only condone such indecency but take part in it was beyond my understanding.

As I got into my car I thought about the other teachers who were present at the party. I wondered how many felt the same as I did but went along with it "for their own good," because of "the Principal's approval."

17

Mr. Towers was noticeably absent from the goof sheet when I signed in the next morning. Then the secretary told me he wanted to see me in his office. I wondered ruefully if sneaking out on a filthy movie was considered insubordinate enough to deserve a private interview.

When I went into his office, I found not only Principal Towers but Lieutenant Swartz from Juvenile detail, and Billy Parrish. In contrast to the night before, Mr. Towers sat slumped in depression behind his desk, his face wearing a cadaverous look. "Morning, Brent," he said heavily. "We've been waiting for you."

I looked at Billy, whose eyes were planted to the floor, then at the lieutenant, who nodded grimly. "Hello, Brent."

"What's wrong?" I asked.

"Billy is one of your homeroom boys so I thought you should know what happened," Towers said gravely. "He was caught in a laundromat last night . . . trying to push a woman into a clothes dryer."

"Billy!" I blurted in horror. "Is that true?"

Mr. Towers said lowly, "I didn't bring you in here to tell you something that wasn't true, Brent."

Lieutenant Swartz spoke up. "The fact is, Mr. Brent, that I called the Principal early this morning and suggested I bring Billy in—so he could hear for himself what we heard last night. You school people have got to know what's going on with these kids. You've got to be on guard against any kid you have who might be a potential threat to an innocent member of our society. And you've got to stop ignoring them and help us do something about them *before* they act—not afterward."

I nodded in sober agreement, recalling only too well the fact that Billy had been simply went to Social Adjustment for throwing a knife in class.

"Okay, Billy," Lieutenant Swartz said wearily. "Tell your teacher and your Principal the story."

Billy's round eyes jerked up to me then at Towers. Then he looked down again. "I was just takin' the initiation rites in the Chain Gang," he mumbled.

"And what are the initiation rites, Billy?" asked the lieutenant.

Billy's jaws worked a moment then he blurted, "You gotta hurt some kid or old geek. Best if you got the guts to hurt some blind or crippled person."

"Go on, Billy," the lieutenant said steadily.

"Well," Billy gulped, "after you cut 'em up, you do the gang devil dance 'round 'em. Then you's in."

The lieutenant said, "Tell them about the woman you were pushing into the clothes dryer."

"Well . . . I been followin' this old cripple around a coupla weeks now. She looked like a pretty good one for me to hurt. . . ."

My stomach churned and my heart pounded with horror as the boy told how he'd figured the clothes dryer at the laundromat was the place to injure his chosen victim . . . how he'd followed her there several times, waiting for the time when there was no one else around. And last night, the time had arrived.

"But I didn't kill nobody," he finished rebelliously. "I didn't even hurt that cripple old woman!"

"But it's not because you didn't try," the lieutenant said harshly. "If you hadn't been caught, you would have hurt her! You probably would have killed her—or made her wish she was dead!"

"She oughta be dead," Billy cried out feverishly. "She'd be outta her misery if she was dead!"

"What kind of a cannibal are you Billy?" I asked.

"Take it easy, Brent," Mr. Towers sighed. "No use getting yourself worked up about it. Billy was caught and it's over. And as he said, the old woman wasn't hurt, after all."

The Principal's words seemed to set the lieutenant afire. "But these people were hurt, Mr. Towers," he said, and opening a large manila folder, he took out three eight by ten glossy photographs, handing them to me.

The first picture showed a woman with an ugly gash

down the side of her face. The lieutenant explained, "The Chain Gang pushed this woman off a bus and performed their initiation rites after they had all raped her in back of a billboard. The driver on the bus, and the handful of passengers, decided to ignore the fact these kids had pushed her off and were dragging her away. As they told us, they decided the police would take care of it." He spoke with bitter irony. "As the woman told us, six or eight youths had assaulted her, cut her face with a switch-blade knife, and then performed a weird dance around her. They then left her, bleeding and almost unconscious. She managed to crawl to the street before she passed completely out."

I could hardly believe it. "You mean that the people on that bus didn't even try to stop those kids? That they just—"

"Most people have a 'leave it to Joe' attitude where trouble is concerned, Mr. Brent," said the lieutenant. "That's the reason I brought Billy in here. It's more important for you school people not to have a 'leave it to Joe' attitude than it is for anybody else."

I looked at the second photograph and the churning in my stomach became an identifiable sickness. It was a picture of a Mexican girl, no more than seven or eight. Her right eye had been gouged out and blood was streaming down her face. Her mouth was open in a look of pathetic screeching.

"That little girl's mother was in the kitchen when she heard her daughter scream from outside," said the lieutenant. "She raced out to the back yard as a gang of boys ran off. Her child was lying unconscious and mutilated on the ground."

Quickly, I passed the picture on to Mr. Towers.

Despite the horror I felt, I couldn't help noticing that he did not look at it, just as he had not looked at the first picture I'd passed on to him.

In the third picture, I saw a man without legs. He was lying on the pavement in front of a wheel chair. Two artificial legs lay tossed beside him. He was bloody.

"This happened last Christmas," the lieutenant said. "Members of the Chain Gang took this man's artificial legs and beat him almost to death with them."

I passed the picture again. Towers did not look at this one, either. He rose and, scowling, said, "This is all rather shattering, Lieutenant, and I'm afraid I don't quite see your point in bringing these monstrous acts to our attention. But I'm sure you have some reason. Believe me, we, as teachers, will do anything we can to help the police—"

"Maybe if you'd help the kids a little more, you wouldn't have to help the police," the lieutenant said gruffly, himself rising. "Come along, Billy."

Billy suddenly smiled up at him. "You think they got room enough down there in Juvenile to hold me, Lieutenant?"

"I think so, Billy," said the lieutenant. "My God, I hope so."

They left, and I started to follow them. Mr. Towers stopped me. "Just a minute, Brent. There are several other matters which I'd like to bring to your attention."

"Yes, sir?"

He sat down heavily. "Number one, my secretary got a phone call just after she'd come in this morning. Whoever the kid was said that a bomb had been planted in the school."

"A *bomb?*" I cried out once again in shock.

"A bomb. But we've had bomb threats before. Let's just hope this one is as false as the others."

"Is that all we're going to do about it—hope?" I asked excitedly. "We've got kids here who could—"

"I'll handle it, Brent, I'll handle it. A thorough search is now being undertaken by policemen and members of the student government."

"But shouldn't we evacuate until—"

"I told you, I'll handle it!" His eyes narrowed into the familiar balls of ice as he stared at me. "Number two, there is a rumble that there's going to be a big showdown between the Chains and the Hoods. The Negro Chains are trying to keep the Negro girls as their own private property. The Hoods, Mexicans, don't want it that way. They are—"

"I believe I heard it was just the opposite," I interrupted. "That the Mexicans don't want to let their girls mingle—"

"Never mind what you heard," he also interrupted. "Before it's over, we'll all have heard it a hundred different ways! My point is that we have some pretty reliable kids who always tip us off when these things are going to happen. As soon as we get the tip-off where and when the showdown is going to take place, we'll have a fleet of police cars ready. The police will speak to the students through the classroom loud speaker system. We'll use the new walkie-talkie communications police station wagon to keep in touch all over the school grounds."

I shook my head in wonder. "It's like preparing for a small-scale, teenage war."

He nodded. "We've got some of the toughest kids in the nation in this school. Not only are they ninety per cent Negro but half of them are bastards."

"And the state is their foster parent," I added soberly. "The state pays for their very existence, actually sponsoring bastardry by doling out welfare to ignorant, irresponsible people every time they produce another child. Eventually, at the rate they're going, they could be in the great majority. They could pick the President of the United States, and determine the whole country's future—or lack of a future."

"Well, there's not much we can do about it," he shrugged. "We've got to help them."

"Are we helping them by paying for their promiscuity? Instead, shouldn't we give them economic opportunity so they can become self-sufficient? Shouldn't we give them a proper education so they can get skilled jobs? They must be taught to accept the challenge of fostering their own welfare and not depend on the state to foster it for them."

Creases lined his troubled brow. "It's easy to say anything, Brent, but it's not always so simple to do it. I know from experience."

"Yes, sir. Well, I'll get to class now."

"Oh, Brent . . ." he stopped me at the door.

"Yes, sir?"

"Some party last night, huh?"

"Yes, sir. It certainly was."

Half-heartedly, he winked a tired eye. "Some movie, too, huh?"

"Yes, sir," I replied evenly. "It was some movie."

18

The bomb scare proved to be just a scare. The showdown did not take place between the Chains and the Hoods. Billy Parrish's removal to Juvenile Hall gave a measure more of peace to my day.

I decided to instill a sense of competition among my Special class students. They were always competing for attention so why not channel them in a productive direction? I made up a chart and told them that each week, the person who wrote the best essay or story would receive an award.

To give them an example, I read a story written by a boy in another class. The boy was one of my brighter pupils and the story held them in rapt interest. My praise of it also tickled the envy of many of them.

"I bet I can do as good as that," Roger Gates asserted.

"Me, too!" Captain Smith piped up.

"You no-count coon," Ruby Burns laughed. "You can't even write your name!"

"Can it be a true story?" Roger asked. His eyes had the glint of a shady character trying to consummate a deal.

"It can be any story," I answered, "true or made up. But be careful of your penmanship and your spelling, as well as the plot. Those things count."

I was surprised during the next few days that, while other of the special students turned in story efforts, Roger failed to since he had seemed the most interested of all in the challenge. By the end of the week, I understood. The others had written fanciful little tales, no more than a few pages long. Roger handed me a notebook thick with pages, and with a proud grin, said knowingly, "That oughta hold you for a piece, Teach."

It did hold me, from beginning to end. I was very tired that night and left Roger's long story till after I had corrected homework papers, intending simply to glance at it and finish it the following evening, but the content of the story was so fascinating that I soon lost myself in it. It was entitled: *Muslim Chop.* It began right at the point:

> "Daddy," I asks, "can you let me go with you tonight to that Muslim chop?"

"You're not going boy. Shut your mouth and do your homework."

I shut my mouth but I decided I was going to figure out some way to go to that swingin meetin when all the cats get together and chop on white man. My old man is no damn good. He wont let me do nothin. I wanna bring some cat over to the house to cool her wagon and he wont let me. I cant drive the car. I cant do nothin. Who the hell does he thinks he is treatin his son like this? All he is is a no good garbage collector. Once I called him Trashman Gates and he whupped my duff so hard I couldn't sit down easy for a week.

I dont go for that Muslim scare shit. I likes the whites. I found me this Spanish chick at school and she likes me. My folks say Ise superior to that white trash but when I holds her close like man I dont care if she is superior or whose inferior. I likes this gal. But her folks act just like my folks. They dont want her to have nothin to do with me. They tell her if she sees me again they will dissown her, what all that means. I call her up and her mother says I cant talk to her or see her or nothin. I see her at school but shes afraid to talk cause her mothers got spies. She pays off gals. I prayed to the devil every night for two weeks to get this chick. Then I thought of a way. I sent her a note. I tells her that if she will meet me I will sneak her into one of those Muslim chops. She met me in our secret place. My old man has a key to this theater where they hold them chops. He picks up trash there. I sneaked his key out and got my own key tooken from it. I knows where I wants to go with my chick. We can hide out up in the projection booth where they used to show the movies. If anyone comes we can hide in the old cabinets. That is a mighty swell place to be with a real nice chick watchin one of them scary ghost Muslim chops.

She tells her mother she got to go see her girl friend and she meets me. The big old dump they calls the Hippodrome is all dark. They dont show nothin there no more. They just rent it out for special things. Nobody got their name up on the front. No broads got their pictures starin at you like theys waiting for you to come close up and look at their great big bodies. Spooky, man.

Anyways, I led this chick down the alley, feelin along in the dark. I put my key in the door and it swings open kinda creaky. I take out my little pencil flash and I wisper "Okay doll lets us cover this crazy jig."

That old dump was so damn spooky my girl grabs my hand and I like that fine. We goes back of the stage and we lifts the old curtins up and climb under. We go down them squeaky steps and up the isle. I put my hand on the wall so I wouldnt fall. Those big old carpets was so thick we didn't make no sound.

We comes out to the big old lobby. We looks in the candy counter. I says to my chick, "Looks like the rats done cleaned it out." She laughs. We go up the steps to the first floor and then up more steps to the second floor. Then we go up more steps. I says, "Baby, we is on top of the hill." She laughs agin. I tries to give her a little kiss but she is all huffin and puffin from climein. I leads her up a little wood staircase and into a hall. I opend the door to the projection room and we go inside. I shuts the door after us. "We safe here, baby," I tells her strong. "You sure?" she asks kind of quivry. "Sure!" I took her then and holds her close and she dont put up no fuss. We have a good time foolin around waitin for the meetin of the Muslim choppers.

Soon the noise of them choppers came like folks comin into a tent meetin. My gal and me we go look out the hole. That big old theater is jammed full. They all starts clappin their hands and shoutin amens. "This all they do?" my chick asks, kind of disappoint. "You wait. They is got a lot they going to do before they thru." I says.

Bout then I could feel my eyes pop open. A great big orchestra just comes right up out a the floor and right up to that stage!!!!!!!!!!!!!!!!!! You never saw nothing like it. Big black studs all decked out in fancy white duds. "They playin battle him of the republick." Chick wispers. I tells her how smart she is and starts to kiss her when a whole bunch of nuts wearin funny white robes come paradin out on that stage. They all carry long poles with sines on the top that say diffrent names of cuntrys. Then the curtin comes up real slow. The stage is all black. Then right in the middle of it some big globe starts lightin up and turnin round and it shoots like stars all over everywhere. The orchestra falls like magick back down inta the floor. A big fat mammy wearing a flashy white dress comes out with a big torch all lit up. An organ starts grindin out some wicked music and that fat mammy sings about goin home. That spaz audence went real wild.

After she done em with her singin, some boss cat comes out and tells everbody that the chop of the Muslims is ready to begin their innanashanal convenshun. He introduce the broad with the boss bass Miss Zita Roda. Them spazzes clap like crazy. Two fags come out and put flowers all around. Some of them spazzes starts yellin "Glory to god we got Roda!" Halleluya and glory be! All that spaz stuff.

Then that weirdo broad gets down on her knees.

She stares up at the crazy spinnin globe, liftin her arms and shakin all that meat like it was gonna come flyin off. All the cats with the poles go and sit in the audence. Everybody hushes up. Roda stands up, all by her self on stage and a mike comes up out a the floor. She speaks and says, "Friends, brothahs, famly." And them spazzes go bats all over agin. Hollerin and clappin like the walls is gonna tumble like old Jerrico, man!

She hushes em up and then she tells them dum cats they all Gods peeple. She says the blacks got to stick up for the blacks and not to mess with the whites evah. My chick gets scared. She says they mite kill her if they find her. I grabbed her close and told her anybody touch her I kill em good!!!!!!!!!!!! I took out my good old knife and show it and man I mean it!!!!!!!!!!! I dont go for that Roda shit. I like my Spanish chick and no big fat-ass mammy is gonna tell me I cant have her!!!!!!!!!!! I prays to the devil for her and he gimme her and I fight God, the devil, the Muslims, the whites, and evry dam nigger on this here earth to keep that woman!!!!!!!! And anybody who reads this here better know it!!!!!!!!!

Then Gawdamighty, we hears steps comin. I starts to shake but I dont wont my chick to know. I grabs her real quick and we runs and hides in the big cabnets. They was so messed up with dust I hases a real urge to coff but my scare wont let me. I thinks maybe I has turned as white as my chick. Ha ha.

We hears the door open and theres some footsteps and clatterin round. I can tell whoever it is is loadin up the old projector. My uncle Ed who is high class who works for the city too but not a garbage man, he works in the place where vots come to, hes got a projector and all that stuff but his dont groan and squeak like that old thing. My uncle Ed is swell, he lets my cousing Boots use his car, lets him bring chicks home. Dont know why nobody would name their son Boots but I sure wish I was lucky like him. Me I got to be foxy for everything I get. Some day I aim to out fox em all!!!!!!!!!!!!

Anyway old Roda her voice comes up from far away and she tells them spazzes she is gonna show pictures from all over the world bout how awful bad the whites treat the blacks. There is a bunch of amens and halleluyas from the spazzes and then some stud starts talkin along with whatever flicks they showin. He says evry cuntry makes the black man do the dirty work and the blackest blacks get the crappyest deals. How the black man he got to pick up garbage. And me I was thinkin how my old man oughta be made to eat it. He a real mean son a bitch!!!!!!!!!!!

Anyway he talked on bout how the famlies even the little kids were out there pickin cotton and that there old man got 40 cents a hour. He says they dont have no winders in their shak and there toylet is outside and they got no good cook stove and nothin to cook on it sept collods. Then he starts on some white man who is rich and the way he say it it sound like it is a sin to be rich. Ha ha. Old Roger is gonna be rich cause he is foxy. I bet them crazy Muslim studs and the broads like this Roda who get the blacks all hot and bothehed would not do it if they wasnt gettin rich. I bet if they wasnt makin money fast and slipry theyd say to hell with the garbage man and the nigger kids workin in the Dixie cotton fields. Let em take care of thereselfs!!!!!!!!!

Anyway they was showin and this man was talkin

about how butiful this place was where this rich man boss lived. About all the flowers and grass and stuff and the swimmin pool big enuff to go boat ridin in. He says about the snazzy cars. One was somethin he called a Roise Rollys. And there was a Cad and one of them neat T birds. He says they drink mint tulips all day and all nite and they got 40 rooms in their pad.

Anyway there was a lot more of that kind of jazz bout how awful hard the blacks have it and how awful good the whites have it. And a lot of times some of them nutty spazzes would shout out real mad like somebody had hold of there tale. Then that movie was done. Fat ass Roda is yellin but I cant here her cause the creeps are doin somethin with the projector but I dont care. My chick is snugglin up close.

They get thru those creeps and I hear the door close shut. I wait a piece then I take my chick and we sneak out again. We look out the hole. Old Roda is still goin on with her bizness shoutin bout how she worked 8 years to get enuff loot to come on over here. She says she got educated. She worked from light up to sun down to keep her fat old machine goin. Whilst other cats was laughin and drinkin and cattin round old Roda was makin big plans. Them dam spazzes clapped there knuckles like nuts.

Roda says she was blessed. Said God did come to her and told her she was gonna lead the black man out of darkness. Just like Moses led the Izraylites out of some hell hole back in olden times. She says she is gonna swing the black peeple out a the chains of slavry and they gonna rule the world. The spazzes screamed and houled. She says, "Is the U.S.A. got freedom for all?" The spazzes hissed and yelled a big fat NO! ! ! ! ! ! ! ! ! ! ! ! ! She says, "Is black man treated equal in U.S.A.?" The spazzes thundered like one of them lightnin storms in Frankenstien movie.

Then the organ began spittin out one of them real cool songs till Roda put up her big fat arms and hushed everbody up again. She says that tonight she was gonna call on the holy ghosts and the dear departed spirits. The white light on her goes to a little green fuzzy light whilst she goes on her knees again. She lifts up her arms and starts wailing like a spook to somebody whose ded. She says to come and tell her peeple what Jesus done told her in a vishun bout black man bein God's children and how Jesus is gonna make the white man pay hard for his sins aginst the black.

Real sudden some big thing zipped across the whole place. Like a red piece of lightnin it was. Scared the shit out a me and scared my chick too cause she grabbed me and I grabbed her back. And lookin down at that audence I think them all was as scared as us were. Some kind of funny spooky smoke came from somewhere. Then some kind of real giant spooky thing that looks sort of like the lines of a man's hed comes fuzzy like thru the smoke. It was like his face was movin, like when you get mad, and there was two big eyes all red and spittin fire. Scaryer then any monster I ever saw in any movie. Then it started out talkin! ! ! ! ! ! ! ! ! It had a voice like come from the ded. It said how he had been a slave in Dixie and had been all beat up all the time but when he had given up the terble life he lived and gone to meet Jesus, Jesus had told him that the white man had to pay. He had told him that the white man was inferior and the black man was superior. He said the devil owned the white man's soul and it was right for the black man to hate the white man cause evil nasty blood was in his vanes. He said the blacks should do everthing they could to take the whites power away. Hit the whites in the pocketbook he says. Give bizness to black man and not to jew. Cept when it came to pushin the white man out. Save money and buy houses where white man lives. Go to places where white man eats. March in lines demandin the rights that white man has. All kind of crap like that. Then he says somethin that was real dirty. Somethin about perocaratin or somethin but which I figured meant havin babies. He was actual flyin up there near the ceilin and tellin everbody to go screw! ! ! ! ! ! ! ! ! ! ! He said the more blacks in the world, the more there would be to take the power away from the whites.

Then there was a sound like thunder and that old spook shouted to KILL THE WHITE DEVILS. The spazzes started shoutin it and kept it up like some crazy chant. My chick starts cryin and I dont blame her. I wants to cry too. Its all so dam nutty.

The ochestra comes up out of the floor agin playin that battle him agin and everbody was stompin and hollerin and carryin on like they was mad. The spook goes back to where he come from and the old curtin falls down on the stage. The spazzes start movin out, still all whupped up. I sort of just stood there, feelin funny, while my chick went on cryin, till that hell hole was empty. The lights went out finely. But I still waited a piece cause I didnt wont no crazy nigger killin my chick cause she is white.

At last we sneaked out a that old rat hole and I nevah want to go consortin with the devil agin! ! ! ! ! ! ! ! ! ! ! !

I closed Roger's notebook and placed it on top of the papers on my desk. The spelling was unbelievably bad. The sentence structure was that of a first grader. The line of thought was often disrupted. However, the penmanship was meticulous, far better than he had ever done before. And he either had the most vivid imagination of any student I'd yet encountered or an uncanny memory for detail.

I decided to give him the award for the week . . . and see what he would come up with next.

The next day, Mr. Towers called me into his office. He got right to the point. "One of our boys was changing his clothes in the gym when Instructor Burke noticed something unusual about his privates. He sent the boy over to the health office. He has gonorrhea. It's too bad, of course, but what is worse is that we can't get out of him the name of the girl, or girls, he's been fooling around with. If we can't determine the female factor, we're dead, and an epidemic of VD could hit the school. I'm talking to all the boy's teachers, trying to find out the girl, or girls, as I said, that he's been seen with. The boy is George Washington."

I stiffened in surprise. "George Washington? Why, he's one of my best students!"

The Principal sighed. "Being a good student has nothing to do with sex, Mr. Brent. Do you happen to know of any girls that George has actively gone around with?"

I shook my head. "No, I don't."

"Well, I'm just checking. We think we know who the girl is but in a case like this, we have to be overly cautious. We sure as hell don't want an epidemic." He leaned back, breathing wearily. "Geraldine Robinson, another of your students, was taken down to Juvenile today. She's pregnant. But she won't talk, either. When she was asked who she'd been having sexual intercourse with, she said *who hadn't* she been having it with. But ten to one, she's our female factor. I just hope she's the only factor."

There are some things you know you can't keep from happening, and some things you wish with all your heart you could. I remembered the foul sight and breath of Geraldine's father . . . and talking with her in the hall . . . and tears welling into her eyes.

And I found that as I drove out of the parking lot, I wasn't heading home. I was going downtown, toward Juvenile Hall.

Wearing a stale grey uniform, Geraldine came meekly into the visiting room. When she saw me, her great, dark eyes lit up for a fraction of a second. Then she sat down and stared at her hands, clenched tightly together in her lap.

"I'm sorry about all this, Geraldine," I said quietly. "Is there anything I can do for you?"

She bit her lip and mumbled, "Thanks, Mr. Brent, but everything's okay. In a lot of ways, being here is a hell of a lot better than being home."

I nodded understandingly. "You have a pretty rough time at home, don't you?"

Momentary fire lighted her face. "You just bet your sweet old ass I do! That damn old Daddy of mine, he beats me to a bloody pulp when his booze is gone! He always gets it stuck in his brain I stole it!"

"You should have reported his beatings to the authorities, Geraldine," I told her, feeling a nauseating surge of disgust rising within me. "They would have taken care of it."

"Nobody takes care of nothin'," she blurted. "Sometimes I thought about killin' that rotten old Daddy of mine! He gets drunk enough, and he makes me go out and get laid for money, so's he can buy more whiskey!"

"Where's your mother, Geraldine?" I asked softly, feeling the tears well behind my own eyes.

"She's dead. And you know something, Mr. Brent? Nobody ever gave a damn about me since Mama died. And you know something else? I don't even give a damn about myself!"

A great sob caught in the girl's throat and she bent over, her face in her hands, weeping softly. I realized then that much of the rebellion and antagonism my children vented on me was only a reflection of the whirlpool of confusion and misery within them.

"Oh, I wish Mama was still alive, Mr. Brent!" Geraldine gasped. "She was a kind lady! She used to dress me all up and take me to Sunday School! And Mama would help me now. She wouldn't let them lock me up like a criminal!"

"Geraldine, you're lucky to have the memory of such a good mother who loved you," I said quietly. "Hold onto that memory. Don't let the rottenness in anyone or anything destroy the goodness in you."

She looked up at me with streaming, tragic eyes. "But what am I going to do, Mr. Brent? What's going to become of me and—and my baby?"

"Do what your mother would want you to do. She'd want you to be brave, to have courage and hope. If it isn't possible for you to make a home for your baby, then see to it that the baby does have a good home. See to it that your baby won't have to suffer the way you've suffered. It's a new little human being, Geraldine. A new life, a new chance, another beginning."

She stared at me through her tears a long time, and I

could tell she was thinking deeply about my words. Then she said in a hoarse whisper, "Thanks, Mr. Brent. You know—you're the first person who really sat down and talked with me—and was interested in me—in a long time. I appreciate it."

Hesitantly, I asked, "Do you know who the father of the baby is?"

She shook her head dumbly.

"Do you have any idea?"

"No, sir. For all I know, this baby could be half white."

Still hesitant, I asked, "Is there—is there a possibility that George Washington could be the father?"

Surprise flickered in her eyes. "George? Why, no! Everybody knows that George don't fool around with any of the girls. They call George old blue-nose. He's too stuck-up to fool around with any of us—" her eyes fell, "—us trash."

"You are not trash, Geraldine," I said firmly, "and I want you to stop thinking about yourself that way. You are a young girl who has unfortunately been forced to live under extremely difficult conditions. But you have your whole future ahead of you, Geraldine. It can be a good future. You can have a good life. But there is only one person in the world who can make your future and your life good. And that's you! And remember one other thing. You may not know who the father of your baby is, but we all truly have one Father we can always depend on, and that's God. Ask God, your Father, and your baby's Father, to help you and give you comfort. Believe me, He will."

A feeble flicker of a smile crossed her face. "Mama

used to say a special little prayer to me when she put me to bed. She used to say, 'God, our Father, in thee we trust. We put our hands in yours for You to lead us with your everlasting love to Heaven'."

"Say that prayer to yourself now, Geraldine," I told her. "Say it over and over again. Because it's true."

I left shortly after that, with the promise that I'd come to see her again, and that if she needed any legal help in the handling of her baby, I'd see to it that she got the best.

I was thoughtful as I drove home. They hadn't told me that teaching only begins in the school. They hadn't told me that it neither begins nor ends there.

When I got home I found a letter waiting for me from my Uncle Tom who lives in Chicago. I opened the envelope to find a newspaper clipping. In the upper corner of the clipping he had written, "Be careful, Bob!"

I read the clipping:

"Fourteen year old Negro, Lee Arthur Hester, saw his favorite teacher working alone in a school storage room. He pulled out a penknife and stabbed her seven times."

I read further: "Lee Arthur Hester could have been examined by the Chicago Board of Education's Bureau of Child Study, but its 83 psychologists are swamped under a waiting list that usually numbers 10,000."

In explaining his motivation the boy had simply stated: "I had to prove I wasn't chicken!"

19

Like a great broom, seventy-mile per hour gusts of wind had swept the city clean of smog. The uninhibited California sunshine was warm on my face through the windshield as I drove to school. Traffic moved swiftly and I had no worries about being late.

Mr. Towers greeted me in an unusually pleasant manner and I went to my classroom. George Washington was waiting outside the door. I had debated in my mind whether or not to mention his trouble and decided against it. It was bad enough for the kid, having contracted a venereal disease. Why rub it in that it was common knowledge among his teachers?

His enthusiasm was a little more subdued than usual when he greeted me. "Hi, Teach. A pretty swingin' mornin', huh?"

I smiled. "It's beautiful, George. A perfect day."

We went into the room and he opened the windows. "Hey, Teach, what you doin' in the Frolics?" he asked.

I looked at him blankly. "Frolics?"

"The Faculty Frolics. Ain't you hip to the big show, man?"

"I guess I'm not."

"It's a big shin-dig the faculty puts together every year," he explained. "Cool, man, cool!"

I checked the bulletin and read. "ATTENTION FACULTY . . . We will have our first Faculty Frolics rehearsal this afternoon in the Multi-Purpose Room. 3:05. There will be no excuses for nonattendence. Punctuality please."

"Mr. Brent . . ." I looked up. George was standing in front of my desk, a serious expression on his expressive young face.

"Yes, George?"

"Did you—er—hear about this little jam I got myself into?" he asked quietly.

I slowly nodded. "Yes, George, I heard about it."

He sighed with all the weariness of mankind. "I tell you, a man can sure find himself behind the eight ball 'fore he even knows what's happened."

"That's right, George," I said soberly. "But you know, if it was one of the girls in school, you really should report it. You might help prevent an epidemic in the school."

He shook his head. "It wasn't nobody from around here, Teach. This black gal's an older woman—must be twenty-four or twenty-five, at least. She's a swingin' stripper got in my path one night and, man, she just wouldn't let go!"

I frowned. "George, you're still a minor. This woman could be charged with contributing to your delinquency."

He smiled with a kind of age-old wisdom. "Teach, man, if they arrested everybody who contributes to the delinquency of a minor, they'd have to build a new county jail to hold all of 'em!"

"Well," I sighed, sitting down, "I just hope you've learned a lesson."

"You bet I have!" He grinned broadly. "Don't fool around with no older gals, and most particularly, when they're strippers!"

The bell rang and my homeroom boys came stampeding in. The day hustled by, and almost before I knew it, I was in the Multi-Purpose room. I sat down next to Miss Joseph and waited for the rehearsal to begin.

"What's this all about?" I asked curiously.

"Oh, it's always a panic," she said wryly. "A regular stage show. The main idea is to let your hair down. That way, you're supposed to let the kids know you're human."

"I don't feel very human," I said drily. "I feel like a machine which has been trained to light up when the taxpayers push coins into it. I work automatically, shoving unbaked brains through me and, periodically, I vomit them out with a phony diploma."

She laughed. "You've been fretting again, Mr. Brent. You should know better by now."

"It's the craziest machine ever," I went on with a sour smile, "because everybody hits the jackpot. You can't lose . . . not even Captain Smith can lose. The only ones who might think they're losing would be a few rare, enlightened taxpayers who keep pumping money in along with the others but who might be a little disturbed by the great quantity of output as compared to the small quality."

"Your bitterness is showing," she said archly, "and it isn't worth it. Forget about it."

When all the teachers were present, Mr. Towers stood below the stage and called us to attention. "People, let's try to get here on time for all rehearsals," he said good-naturedly. "This is the first one and already we're running a few minutes behind schedule. This show means a lot to the morale of the kids in this school. It's the one time in the year we can unbend and let them know we're human just like them. Let your hair down and have a ball. This is an excellent form of communication."

Communication, I thought, the one thing I'd been failing in for so long. Perhaps this would be the chance I needed to help me find the common denominator in reaching my students. I listened attentively.

"First, we'll divide into groups," announced the Principal, and he began rattling over a series of activities and names. My name was included in Group D. "Group D will present a one-act skit called 'A Day In School.' Dress in costumes appropriate for an eleven year old. We'll begin the school day with a jazzed-up version of the bugle call. For the pledge of allegiance to the flag, we have written a comical verse . . ."

Everyone in Group D was given a carbon copy of the comical verse. I read: "I pledge allegiance to Mr. Towers, our mentor, and to the school in which he sits, one man, among men and women, with laughter and pleasure for all—the dirty rat!"

I couldn't believe it! Stiffly, I raised my hand.

"Yes, Brent?"

"Mr. Towers, do you mean you actually expect me to recite this nonsense while saluting our flag?"

An immediate hush fell over the faculty. Towers stared at me evenly a moment then, with a forced laugh, said, "It's all in fun, Mr. Brent."

"To me, the flag is a sacred symbol," I said firmly. "I can in no way make fun while pledging allegiance to it."

He put on his frozen smile. "You're new, Mr. Brent, so you probably don't understand the purpose of this assembly. I'm sure that if you'll just sit calmly and quietly and let us continue, you'll see that your apprehensions are completely unjustified."

I sat back and he went on doling out hogwash to his loyal followers. The longer I sat, the more incensed I became. Had the policy of this school become "nothing sacred"? Did "unbending" and showing the students we were "human" mean that we must shuck every last morsel of dignity we possessed?

When we were dismissed, I found that I was actually trembling with rage. Miss Joseph, filing out beside me, said in a cryptic whisper, "You really don't care about Towers, do you?"

"Not if it means being in a program like this to get a good rating!"

I went directly to the office and waited for Mr. Towers. When he came in and saw me, his jaw set firmly and he eyed me suspiciously. "Well, Brent?"

Trying to maintain a calm I did not feel, I said, Mr. Towers, I'm afraid I cannot participate in your Faculty Frolics."

"Is that so?" he asked, his voice tinged with ominous overtones. "What are you doing, witch-hunting again?"

"Call it whatever you like," I retorted angrily, "but from what I heard just now I think some witch-hunting had better be done around here!"

His face crimsoned. "That's enough, Brent! I can only take your remarks as insubordination!"

"If it's insubordination to refuse to take part in a program that not only makes fun of the flag, but ridicules the very decency we're striving so hard to instill in these kids, then that's what it is! I'd turn in my resignation before I'd be a party to it!"

"Maybe that's what you'll end up doing, Brent. Turning in your resignation." Swiftly, he went into his private office, slamming the door behind him.

Heatedly, I left school. I had never considered visiting the Board of Education before but now I wanted to. I'd heard so much talk about not being extreme in my views, not being over-American, but now I wondered if someone, someplace, might have a speck of fear that a teacher could be *under*-American!

I went to see one of the heads of a teacher's organization. He listened soberly as I told him about the prospective Faculty Frolics, and my supposedly insubordinate attitude. Finally, he said he would go with me to see Mr. Never, the man who was in charge of teacher complaints at the Board. "But let me warn you," he added drily. "For a teacher to criticize a superior is about as dangerous as to make hamburger from a Hindu holy cow."

Mr. Never greeted us pleasantly and we sat down. He was a small, wiry man who looked as if he were constantly ready to yawn. "Well, what can I do for you gentlemen?" he asked.

"Mr. Never, I have found that I disagree with the method in which various activities are handled at the school where I teach," I told him. "However, I fully realize that there must always be a variance of viewpoint concerning many things."

"Yes, yes, go on," he murmured.

"There is one matter upon which I feel confident you'll agree. There must be absolutely no division of opinion about this." I handed him the carbon copy of the comical pledge to the flag, explaining, "I have been asked to recite this before the student body while saluting the United States flag, and I consider it un-American and sacriligious."

He read the pledge slowly, then looked at me without expression. "Who ordered you to do this?" he asked.

"The Principal of the school, Mr. Towers."

He sat back, and folding his hands over his stomach, said, "Mr. Brent, let me tell you what our policy is down here at the Board. If your Principal tells you to do something, you do it."

"But—"

"If he tells you to stand on your head or swing by your teeth, Brent, you do it!"

Hot anger rose inside me again. "I might stand on my head and I might swing by my teeth, sir, but I will never make a mockery of the United States flag!"

He stared at me rather indifferently. "Then you'll have to take the consequences, I'm afraid. If your Principal formally charges you with direct insubordination it could mean the loss of your job."

I rose. "I have certain principles to maintain, Mr. Never, and none of those principles could ever be bought from me by the wages I make as a teacher—or for any amount of money."

"You're entitled to your opinion," he shrugged.

"I'm beginning to think I'm entitled to no opinion at all in this system! How can I inspire character in my children if I'm allowed to have none myself?"

"I said you were entitled to your opinion, Mr. Brent," he said evenly. "I didn't say you were entitled to act upon that opinion. Nor to rebel against your superiors and the system."

"I think that if this system were exposed as approving mockery of the flag, it would be thrown out by indignant, shocked American mothers and fathers," I said angrily. "I don't think many of them want their children to be taught that there is nothing sacred—not even the flag!"

"You've said your piece, Brent," Never said in a low voice. "Now I think you'd better go."

The fact that I had visited the Board was never mentioned by Mr. Towers. Nor was any pressure put on me to participate in the Faculty Frolics. It was as if I weren't even there.

At last, the great show-day arrived. All the kids were

noisily excited over the coming event, scheduled to take place after school.

The auditorium was a minor bedlam, supervision resting solely in the hands of student government. Finally, when the high school band struck up, they were able to manage some semblance of order.

The house lights slowly dimmed down to darkness. The band blared loudly with some cancan music. The maroon velvet curtains opened. Lights came up on the stage, bare except for a blue curtain backdrop.

Suddenly, across the stage, a chorus of flimsily-clad, high-stepping lovelies appeared, their hairy legs rising awkwardly in the cancan, their arms entwined, their grapefruit bosoms bouncing jauntily in time to the music. They were ten of the male teachers.

The audience of children laughed, cheered, and clapped their hands hysterically. Their hysteria rose into wild abandon at Instructor Burke, dressed as a policeman, raced onto the scene with a billy-club and drove the exhibitors of the historically indecent dance off the stage. I somberly recalled when Khrushchev refused to be photographed at Twentieth Century Fox Studios during a cancan dancing scene because he felt the dance symbolized decadence. I wondered what his comment would be if he saw the teachers of American children performing the same dance in front of those children, as unskilled as it might have been.

Mercifully soft strains of music from the Swan Lake ballet came over the loud-speaker system. The stage lights darkened and then a soft blue light appeared, barely revealing a figure pirouetting onto the stage. The light slowly became more intense. The figure, in a female ballet costume, belonged to one of the male teachers, particularly paunchy and ungraceful. He pretended to trip over his own feet and fell flat on his paunch on the floor, much to the riotous delight of his students who were watching. Another male teacher, clad in ballet tights, and wearing a blonde wig, minced quickly across the stage to the unfortunate dancer's rescue. He tried to help him up and the two of them became involved in a Keystone Kops comedy routine which brought the house down. The blonde wig flew into the audience and there was such a scramble for it among the children that the show was almost stopped. And too bad it wasn't.

The recording of Swan Lake was put on the wrong speed, and the two dancers cavorted madly, trying to keep pace with the mad music. The curtains then closed on what I thought rather sadly, might possibly be the only exposure to good music some of these children would ever have. If this type of thing was "communication," I thought, then I was glad I was not communicating.

I was wondering how they were going to top this for laughs when the curtain opened again and the high school band began grating and grinding some twist music. In black hose, tight skirts slit up the sides, and skin-hugging sweaters, members of the female portion of the faculty wiggled and bounced onto the stage, forming a twisting semicircle.

Over the loud-speaker, a voice announced, "With the help of our hep audience, we will now pick the top teacher twister! First, Miss Steele, of the Home Economics Department!"

Tall, gangling, grey-haired Miss Steele gyrated to

center stage and twisted amazingly, with rhythmic accuracy, to the music—if you can call it that. The house went down in applause. I thought with some disgust that if she couldn't waggle a good report from Mr. Towers, she could always wiggle in burlesque.

The other female teachers all had a turn at center stage, including Miss Joseph, whose petite, prematurely matronly figure appeared ludicrously off balance and out of place performing the twist.

"Shake it but don't break it!" One of the boys in the audience called out excitedly, and it was followed by more bedlam, with the kids twisting in their seats in time to the music, screeching like young savages.

The voice from the loud-speaker system broke over the noise. "For the grand finale of the Teacher Twisting Contest, we present Mrs. Ratterman, the girls' gym teacher!"

From backstage, Mrs. Ratterman twisted out, her buxom buttocks poured into tight, gold lamé gym trunks. She twisted around the fringe of the stage, cavorting, bending, and all in all, performing obscene movements heretofore confined to burlesque and the boudoir but now a national pastime for the kiddies. The kiddies in our school reacted thunderously, many of them rising from their seats and imitating her motions down the rows and the aisles.

"Shave it off!" A boy's voice cried loudly.

"Suck it off!" Someone else shouted.

I wondered if anyone other than myself, in the excitement, had heard these vulgar cries from the kids in the audience.

The music stopped, the dancers stood still, breathing heavily, and the voice on the loud-speaker announced,

"Our hep audience has decreed Mrs. Mabel Ratterman the winner!"

As the music struck up again, the children stomped their feet, clapped, and whistled their approval, while Mrs. Ratterman obligingly twisted back into the spotlight and gave a vigorous encore. Evidently carried away by the music and the applause, she quieted only when the president of the student body came on stage and presented her with a small statuette in recognition of her achievement.

When the curtains came together and the children were finally reduced to a semblance of discipline, another of the female gym teachers stepped in front of the curtain. She was wearing a formal gown, conservatively cut. The organ began playing an unfamiliar melody and the woman sang in a mild soprano incomprehensible words which I believed had something to do with the United Nations. When she was through, there was a smattering of applause, a few groans, and one loud catcall.

Next came the comedy skit, "A Day In School." The curtains parted, revealing about ten desks set in a make-believe school room. The teacher's desk and the flag were at the front of the room. I found that I was scarcely breathing. By the fact that nothing had been mentioned to me about my visit to the Board, and that I had not been called upon to contribute to the program after my resolution, I'd suspected that even though I'd seemed to have reached no understanding with Mr. Never, words of warning might have been sent out and any mockery to the flag dispensed with.

Not only was I wrong about that but even worse affronteries to education than I'd dreamed possible were enacted.

The voice of the Boys' Vice-Principal came over the loud-speaker system. He said in sugary tones, "Good morning, boys and girls. This is Mickey Mouse. Be good today and sell your cookies for the cookie drive! And don't forget, this above all, to Mr. Towers be true!"

A male teacher came on stage, moving behind the desk. A female teacher, dressed as an eleven-year-old, ran on with a huge apple in her hands. She gave it to the teacher. At the moment he took it, a giant worm sprouted forth from it. The other make-believe eleven-year-olds raced onto stage and to their desks. The bugle call sounded and they stood for the pledge of allegiance to the flag. The bugle call broke into hot jazz notes which came from a trumpet over the loud-speaker system. The audience laughed loudly as the hot bugle call paid disrespect to our flag.

Then the make-believe students began to recite, and I found my breath coming faster. I had won! They were not reciting the mockery to the flag which I had complained about but the actual pledge of allegiance. Whether it had been Mr. Towers' after-and-more-wise thought or a suggestion sent in from the Board, I had finally made some small dent in the bureaucratic system! At least they weren't making fun of something which should be sacred not only to the children but to each and every teacher—to each and every American in our country.

Yes, I had won that victory but I was in for a similarly disturbing performance. When the pledge was over, the fire alarm buzzer sounded loudly from backstage.

The make-believe students on stage rushed wildly around the room, falling over desks, bumping into each other, and creating such a confused commotion that if they had actually been warned about a fire, all of them would have been trapped, no doubt, before they could have reached safety. I truly did not see how they could find any sense of comedy in a fire drill, particularly when eight small fires had already been set that year by an unknown pyromaniac.

The rest of "A Day At School" proceeded in the same mocking manner. There was an A-bomb drill to which no heed was paid. Every time the teacher ordered, "Drop!" the students pretended to think he was giving them a spelling drill and immediately started shouting in unison, "D-r-o-p!" There were fist-fights, arguing and bickering, and seldom could the teacher's voice be heard above the students'—much to the delight of the audience of students.

The picture of a typical Day At School might have been fairly accurate, if you wanted to judge it on mayhem. But it was far from being comical to me, as the typical day was far from comical. The fact that the teachers and the principal of the school would paint such awful truth as being more humorous than paganistic gave me the feeling I had the substance of a dry bone in my mouth. I could not only not chew it, I could never swallow it.

When the skit was over, the curtain closed and the band played a march. The house lights went on, and the Girls' Vice-Principal came gaily on stage and spoke into the microphone. "We've enjoyed the Faculty Frolics, haven't we?"

The audience thundered their agreement. She lifted her hands, quieting them. "And now, students, we are going to present a gift to our wonderful Principal, Mr. Towers, from the Student Association and the Faculty Association. We want to show him how we appreciate his sponsorship of this program and all the fine assemblies he makes possible."

Mr. Towers grinned his way on stage, standing straight and proud beside the Girls' Vice-Principal. The student body president ran on, handed the woman a large, ribbon-wrapped box, and ran off again. She untied the ribbon, and with overly sincere dramatization, said, "We, the members of the Student Association and the Faculty Association, give you this gift that you deserve, Mr. Towers, as no other Principal deserves it. This gift is the token of our regard for your judgment, kindliness, and consideration throughout the year. We give you this gift to show you exactly what we think of you!"

With that, she put the box on the floor, lifted out of it a big, whipped cream pie, and with perfect aim, threw it directly into Mr. Towers' face. The students burst into another fit of joyous hysteria, while the Principal stood there, swaying back and forth with his own deep laughter. He then wiped the whipped cream pie from his face with both hands, and smeared it onto the face of the shrilly giggling girls' Vice-Principal.

The curtain closed. The student body president ran in front of the curtain and in an imitation of Bugs Bunny, shouted, "Th-th-that's all, folks!" The Faculty Frolics had ended. And as far as I was concerned, the symbols of authority the school represented had ended, too. As I filed out of the auditorium with the wildly enthusiastic children, I wondered how I could ever again send one of them to Mister-Pie-In-The-Face Towers for discipline or correction. And then I thought, that was perfect symbolism for the system, wasn't it? I was asked to give these children pie-in-the-sky dreams with meaningless, frothy grades. All you had to do was poke your finger through those grades and their value would vanish. There was nothing there but an illusion of substance.

20

For days the students talked enthusiastically of the Faculty Frolics and they were, in the afterglow of the Frolics, more unmanageable than ever. The fact that I had not participated in the "big show" seemed to alienate me from the rest of the faculty. I wondered if it were because I had not valued my job above my integrity while many of them, though disliking it as heartily as I, had "gone along" with such asinine ridicule because it was a dictum from the Principal, by the Principal, and because of the Principal. I wondered if the teaching profession had sunk to the level of believing, "This above all, to the Principal be true," the way the educational system obviously had.

Several days after the Frolics, Mr. Towers called me into his office. Never had I seen him so red of eye and snarling of lip. He looked like a starved lion ready to be uncaged to attack any victim who might fall into his path. Nor did he hesitate.

"Brent, I've received several threatening telephone calls! Some of the parents seem to have been told that I showed disrespect for the flag by jazzing up the bugle call in the Frolics. What do you have to say about this?"

"What do you mean?" I asked warily.

He jumped to his feet and, rounding the desk, came threateningly toward me. "I mean that I think you're responsible! I think you've contacted these parents and deliberately tried to agitate them against me!"

"I've done nothing of the sort," I said angrily, rising. "I am not a rabble-rouser, Mr. Towers! If the parents called you and told you what they thought, perhaps it *was* the way they thought, not simply the way someone told them to think!"

"I'm just as patriotic as you are," he yelled unreasonably, "and don't you think I'm not! The trouble with you is that you don't have any sense of humor! You *are* a rabble-rouser and a witch-hunter, and I know you're out to make trouble for me, don't think I don't! But let me warn you. I've got a hell of a lot more power in this system than you have! I've worked hard and long getting that power. And beside me you're an amateur! So you'd just better coddle your cookies, kid, and stop trying to act like a professional when you're not!"

When I left his office, I couldn't help thinking about his accusing words. Because a member of his staff refused to agree with his policies, he blamed that member for any outside person who also disagreed. There was no doubt about it. I had not only fallen into his supreme bad graces by having a difference of opinion with him but he now considered me responsible for every other person who did. It was not a very savory position to be in.

Not long after that, Billy Parrish came back to school. He had been right. Juvenile hadn't been big enough to hold him—for long. And despite his failure to do actual bodily harm to his intended victim, he was looked upon with newly-found respect by his cohorts in the Chain Gang for having been "sent up" because he had tried.

As the school year drew to a close, nonacademic activity mounted to such heights that there was little time left for teaching and little energy left for learning. Any attempt demanding study was a farce. I felt as if I were riding some meaningless merry-go-round and looked forward to the last day when it would stop and I could get off.

One teacher was pushed off before it stopped.

"Did you hear about the stabbing?" someone asked as I went into the Faculty Lounge before classes.

"No . . ."

"Guy over at Markham," said someone else.

Miss Joseph came up to me and showed me a newspaper. I read the headline JUNIOR HIGH TEACHER, STABBED, GIRL HELD.

She read, " 'Social studies teacher, Robert Collier, is in satisfactory condition at California Hospital today following what police describe as a "blackboard jungle" stabbing in the halls of Markham Junior High School. His teenage assailant is held in Juvenile Hall on a charge of attempted murder. Collier, 25, was stabbed twice in the right shoulder by a 14-year old student he had disciplined last week for talking in class. The girl used an eight-inch butcher knife. The report states that she had stolen the weapon from her mother's kitchen.

" 'While Collier was walking down the hall during a class change, the girl approached him from the rear and stabbed him once, the report continues.

" 'Stunned, the teacher grappled with her for the weapon while other teachers attempted to pull her away. She plunged the knife into him once more before they could subdue her.

" 'Juvenile Sgt. Marie Thomas said the girl told several of her schoolmates that she was going to get the teacher. None would believe her.

" ' "I made up my mind to kill him last Thursday," she reportedly told officers.

" 'Inattention in class had caused Collier to send the girl from the room last Monday, Collier reported to officers.' "

I took the paper and looked at the picture of a Negro girl. Underneath was a caption quote: "I'm only sorry I didn't kill him."

Everyone was talking. "It's Towers' fault. He was over at Markham and he probably let the discipline go to pot there like he's done here."

"He's a good guy but a weak administrator."

"He's too new at the game. Why in hell do they put the new guys on the roughest jobs?"

"What gets me is it could have been any of us."

The voices seemed muted and from a great distance. *It could have been any of us.* It just happened to be Collier. The day Billy Parrish ran around the room with a knife and held it level with my stomach might have been my day.

The bell rang. I wondered if this would be the day the value of a single human life might register on the students' conscience . . . might force them to wake up and see where their path of hatred was leading. There was restless turmoil seething throughout the school. I felt the frenzy from my homeroom class right through to the Special class at the end of the day.

"You shouldn't give no homework today, Teach!" Billy Parrish cried out.

"Why not, Billy?"

"You know what happened to that other stud who gave homework, don't you?"

Captain Smith exclaimed, "I'm gonna write her a letter cause—"

"You no-count coon, you can't write your name," Ruby Burns snapped, as usual.

"He can write anything he damn likes to," Marion Blackwell said hotly. "I'm the fan-club president for that foxie chick that took care of that no-good teach. That twitchin' chick has done more for education than all the spooks in this dump put together. We don't need to take no more o' that scare shit 'bout homework no more!"

As many of the others nodded and mumbled in agreement, I looked at their wrathful young faces. I recalled Helen's words on Thanksgiving about the Negro leader who said he had three hundred thousand Negroes who would mob, rob, steal or kill to get what they wanted. I remembered Roger Gates' story about the Muslim meeting. "Kill the white devils!" *God! what is it coming to?* I thought. In their warped world of hate, they couldn't see any reason not to celebrate an attempted murderer as a heroine! To them, she had done battle with the enemy, and the press was paying her court with full picture coverage.

After school, I drove downtown to see Lieutenant Swartz. He told me that Robert Collier was coming along fine. Then, "Why did the girl do it?" I asked.

"She thought Collier was going to give her an Unsatisfactory on her report card."

"An Unsatisfactory prevents a student from graduating," I nodded, "but for this, she'd kill him?"

"For this, she'd kill him."

I took a deep breath, feeling the weight of hate in action. "Lieutenant, this is a terrible situation, and I don't know what we're going to do about it. These Negro kids are hate-conscious from the time they know the difference between black and white. They use race prejudice like a weapon. They hear it at home. If their fathers get fired, prejudice. If they can't find a job, prejudice. If they don't get the grades they want in school, prejudice."

He nodded somberly. I rose, thanked him for his time, and started out.

"Oh, Brent." He stopped me at the door. "You might like to know . . . Robert Collier is a Negro."

I was stunned. Automatically, I had assumed that Collier was a white man. Had it reached a point where I, too, was seeing things through reflex race prejudice?

Several days later, Mr. Towers called me into his office after school to say, "I'd like you to take charge of the speaking portion of the Memorial Day program. The band teacher will pick the selections for the band and Miss Pritchard, the music teacher, will select the songs for the Glee Clubs. You will work with them and give whichever students you choose speeches to say commemorating the day."

"Thank you very much," I said. "I'll do my best."

He nodded. "Just see that it's good."

As I drove away from school, I was thoughtful. Mr. Towers had bestowed an unexpected honor upon me by giving me leadership of the Memorial Day program; and yet, just a short time before, he had practically accused me of being incompetent. Was it possible that he felt no malice toward me personally but only toward the "me" which represented a physical picture of his own shortcomings? I had certainly pushed those shortcomings into his face often enough.

I tried to put myself in his position. There was no doubt that he had a ruthless dedication to the downtown office. But he also had a wife and five children to support. His job and his assured salary obviously had to mean a great deal to him. Uppermost in his mind was having school affairs run smoothly. When they didn't, he was bound to be upset and feel highly frustrated. At times, he must feel like a line man carrying the ball with everybody ready to tackle him from all sides. Was there any wonder his administration was not picture perfect?

I found myself feeling sorry for him. As so often happens to me when I try to put myself in another's position,

I thought, *there but for God go I.* Thank God, I didn't constantly have to trip the light fantastic and hope the downtown office would applaud.

I went to the Los Angeles Public Library and after several hours had gathered a good collection of books on all the American wars. I planned to have the children capsulize the conflicts and the heroes from the Revolution to the Korean war, paying honor to those who had died in order that we might be living now under a banner of freedom.

It took me several days to arrange a program and to select the children I thought fitted for each portion. When I was finished, I submitted a copy to Mr. Towers for approval. The next morning I found a note in my box instructing me that a conference with Miss Pritchard had been arranged. We were to meet after school. Good, I thought. He liked my ideas and was anxious for the program to be put together.

I was due for still another surprise.

"Mr. Towers has suggested we use this book to form our program," Miss Pritchard told me, giving me a heavy work. "It deals with immigrants who chose America to begin a new life."

Puzzled, I glanced through the book. "Memorial Day is when we are supposed to honor our war dead," I said. "What have these people to do with it?"

She smiled. "Mr. Towers feels it is best to devote our thoughts to peace and prosperity rather than to violence and death."

"But *it is* Memorial Day! It isn't Christmas or Thanksgiving or the Fourth of July!"

"Those are Mr. Towers' orders," she shrugged. "I have chosen to honor Spyros Skouras, Helena Rubinstein, Irving Berlin, and Gian Carlo Menotti. Are they okay with you?"

I sighed. Overwhelmed by the whole idea, but giving in to it, I said, "If we are going to honor such people, don't you think it would be only fair to have one of them a Negro? I mean, with the majority of the kids being Negro, don't you think—"

"Quite right," she nodded. "Why don't we forget about Menotti and use George Washington Carver instead? Oh—and of course, we'll use the Gettysburg Address. That's always nice."

Thus the Memorial Day program took seed. I wrote speeches about what our honored persons had to say concerning America. They were all happy praises for a land where prosperity flourished for all. Miss Pritchard and a crew of students took care of the props.

We had our first rehearsal. Mr. Towers was there. The stage had been carefully decorated. There were four arches. Above one was test tube paraphernalia and a cardboard peanut, symbolizing Mr. Carver. Above another was a huge, painted eye and an eyeshadow brush, symbolizing Miss Rubinstein. Above the third was a musical note and a bar of music, symbolizing Mr. Berlin, and above the arch honoring Mr. Skouras a cardboard replica of a motion picture camera.

"Excellent," Mr. Towers commented happily concerning the stage. "Very professional!"

The students recited their various speeches then the band played several patriotic numbers and the Glee Clubs sang a few patriotic songs. The Gettysburg Address was given by a boy who had an exceptionally good voice.

"Good work, Brent," Mr. Towers beamed.

"Thank you," I said, "but we have several more parts in the program yet."

"Oh?" He nodded appreciatively. "Good, good. We certainly want to have a complete program."

I gave instructions to the boy who was handling the sound equipment. He put on a recording I had bought of President Franklin Delano Roosevelt's speech following the attack on Pearl Harbor. I sat beside Towers and listened. It was truly one of the most stirring statements ever made, and I found tears coming into my eyes as I recalled the confusion and sense of devout patriotism I had felt as a child during those trying days.

I glanced at Towers. His face was a somber mask as he listened.

After President Roosevelt's speech, a recording of Edward R. Murrow's *I Can Hear It Now* was put on the phonograph. Towers sat up and turned to me. "Is this your idea, Brent?"

"Yes, sir," I nodded. "I think both recordings beautifully commemorate—"

"I don't care for either of them."

Another shock. "You—don't?"

He stood abruptly. "I don't. Take them out."

I rose, bewildered. "Yes, sir," I murmured.

"But almost everything else is fine, Brent. Excellent work."

I watched him walk out as Mr. Murrow's deeply moving statements filled the auditorium. I waved to the boy handling the sound equipment, and said, "Okay, that's all." When it was again silent, I said to the others, "The Memorial Day program will begin with *God Bless America* from the Girls' Glee Club, will continue through the speeches of Spyros Skouras, Helena Rubinstein, Irving Berlin, and George Washington Carver, and will end with the Gettysburg Address."

To myself, I said, *forget about it. Do the best you can, get it over with, and forget about it.*

But there were to be further difficulties. For one of the speeches, I had used a shy, coal-black boy who had an unfortunate lisp. When I had worked with him privately, he had mastered his problem and was very proud of it, but when he got on stage the lisp would return. Much as I disliked it, I was afraid to let him continue with the part, not only because he was incompetent in performing before an audience but because I was afraid I would be accused of deliberately picking a Negro boy who lisped in order to give the Negroes a poor showing. If such a fear seemed like cowardice, perhaps it was, but I had learned to tread cautiously on the thin border between black and white.

I gave the part to another boy. It so happened that he was a very light-skinned mulatto. The first boy was very upset, even though I tried to explain to him that before long, if he worked hard to overcome his difficulty, he would be able to perform as well if not better than anyone else.

"That's what you say!" he had cried out defiantly. "It's cause I'm black and he's light, that's why you give him my part!"

He had run out of the room then, leaving me with a feeling that I was hamstrung, but I had thought, *a few tears, a little pouting, and he'll get over it.* I thought about going to see his parents, to suggest some special medical attention for his affliction.

During the next rehearsal, while the mulatto boy was giving his speech, the lights suddenly went off. I rushed backstage. At the same time, there was a crashing sound and a cry of pain. I pulled the light switches back on. My performer was sprawled on the floor, the piano bench upside down a few feet away. He was crying and holding his head. My lisper was running gleefully out the door.

There seemed to be nothing which could be done honestly and simply without creating a problem. I wanted to take the injured boy to the Principal and see to it that the other boy paid for his act of violence, but the young victim pleaded with me to forget about it. "You cause him any trouble and he'll get me after school," the boy whined. "I'll be the one who has got to pay for it!"

Despite a feeling of guilt that I was being lax in necessary disciplinary measures, I decided to drop it, as I had found myself deciding so often lately. It was as if I were treading a tightrope; if I fell off on either side, I wouldn't be the only one who was hurt.

The mother of the lisping boy came to see me, complaining. I tried to explain the situation to her but her final declaration was simply, "All I know is my son didn't get to do the part."

I wondered if there was anything else which could go wrong. There was. The book on George Washington Carver which I had used for the program was stolen from my desk. I had to pay a five dollar fine to the library. A Mexican boy accused a Negro boy of looking up the skirts of the Mexican girl who was playing Helena Rubinstein as she came down the catwalk. In the battle which ensued, the Mexican boy came close to losing an eye.

But somehow the program finally went on. It was met with complete approval by everyone except myself. While I appreciate the fine motion pictures filmed under Mr. Skouras, the patriotic music written by Mr. Berlin, the glamour Helena Rubinstein has given the female sex, and the many uses for the peanut devised by Mr. Carver, I did not think our war dead would have thought their sacrifices appropriately symbolized by a movie camera, a musical note, an eyeshadow brush, and a peanut. As far as I was concerned, the Memorial Day program was a monumental failure. But I said nothing. During the year, I had learned that the squeaking wheel doesn't always get the grease. Sometimes it is simply discarded.

When it was all over, I busily tried to catch up with the mountain of homework I'd had to neglect. It was a depressing business, with the constant bad spelling, the foul words, error upon error. I had continued giving an award for the best story each week but I had changed the award from a candy bar, due to complaints from parents that candy was bad for their children's teeth. Now, I gave tubes of Crest toothpaste. The children's enthusiasm had lessened but, occasionally, some of them came up with fairly decent stories.

There was one that was far from being decent which I read just after the Memorial Day program. It was written by Angelina Childers:

> This story is about one of those hip True Confessions girls who is real bad and knows too much for her age. She is visitin this swingin boss cat whose teasin her all the time. She says Daddio, you let me alone. I don't wanna play in your play pen tonite.

Daddio says he wants to take her to a jig. She says go blow and he grabs her and says he'll give her some bread. She pushes him off the davenport and he goes clear cross that floor on his butt. She laughs her head off. He comes runnin at her and grabs this boss chick and says Shit, girl, I'm not gonna take this crap. She says you no good rat. You live in a garbage can. And he runs out and gets the ax. She yells bloody murder and runs to the toilet. She closes the door and he puts his big fist through that dam door and opens it. He pushed her down and takes that ax and chops her head off. All the gushy, gushy blood comes oozin out. There is a real bloody mess all over that swinging bathroom floor. Then he chops up her body and puts it down the garbage disposal. Then he puts her head in a bucket on the shelf. He mops up the floor with the towels and throws them out the window.

Then that cool cat goes prowlin' and finds himself a woman. He brings her to his pad and he starts makin out. She xcueses herself and goes to the toilet. And that old bucket falls off the dam shelf and that bloody, gushy head goes rollin cross that dam floor. It scares the life outta her, that crazy mixed up hips. She yells and that sex maniak comes for her. He takes that big old ax and swings down hard and her head cames clean off. It goes flyin out that window and falls in the garbage can. He picks up old hips body and throws her out too and she falls in the garbage can like perfect aim. Then that cool cat goes to the berlesk and watches them wicked women shake all over.

I felt helpless in dealing with a girl as mentally and emotionally disturbed as Angelina. I gave up reading, made some coffee, and turned on the television set to catch the evening news. The announcer was saying grimly:

"Today, a tragedy occurred in Griffith Park which will scar the record of no race riots in Los Angeles. It began when three Negro youths sought rides on the merry-go-round without buying tickets. The attendant, a seventy-year-old man, tried to order the youths off the amusement vehicle and they refused to leave. Within moments, a riot started. Someone shouted, 'This is not Alabama,' and the crowd ignited into an angry mob. with milk bottles, baby bottles, thermos jugs, stones, and anything else people could find being hurled at the merry-go-round. Police Chief Parker has stated to the press that he had known this area was a trouble spot for some time. He had prompted police officers there to be prepared for just such a display of violence. Between seventy-five and a hundred policemen came to the scene at which an estimated thousand people were present. One policeman was struck in the head and suffered severe brain concussion. There has never been any segregation in the use of Griffith Park, the world's largest park within the confines of a city. However, the Negroes and the white people have formed their own distinct segregation, and as these films indicate, everyone involved in the actual battle was Negro."

I turned the set off. I felt inundated with hate and violence and didn't want to see or hear any more about it—at least not that night.

During the next few days, I carefully followed the reaction to the riot in the newspapers. On the editorial page of the Los Angeles *Times* was an article headlined NO, THIS IS NOT ALABAMA. It read:

> The Griffith Park episode was, in fact, as far removed from Alabama in its causes as the park is in its geography. . . . There was not a race riot . . . it was an explosion of hoodlumism. . . . The Griffith Park thing was started by a boy full of youthful belligerence. . . . Griffith Park was not a major incident. . . . It can be misinterpreted. In fact, we can depend on it being misinterpreted . . . this editorial is designed to set the record straight. We here in Los Angeles can only exhort our fellow citizens not to draw wrong conclusions from the incident. . . . Only a fool or a conscious mischief-maker would try to apply the Griffith Park incident to local race relations. But there are fools and mischief-makers, and the community must be alert against them. . . . The agitators who will try to use the Griffith Park incident are more dangerous than the hoodlums who crashed the merry-go-round.

In the news section of the very same paper, there was an article headlined TWO MORE SUSPECTS JAILED IN RIOT AT GRIFFITH PARK. It read:

> Police arrested two additional suspects Wednesday in the Memorial Day Griffith Park riot as one of five officers injured in the melee in which more than two hundred persons participated was reported in only "fair" condition at Central Receiving Hospital.
>
> Meanwhile, Police Chief Parker branded the riot as a "racial situation" and said it was undoubtedly stimulated in part by the actions of southern Freedom Riders and the bitter campaigning in the local mayoralty campaign.

It was interesting. The editorial had clearly stated that "only a fool or a conscious mischief-maker would try to apply the Griffith Park incident to local race relations. But there are fools and mischief-makers, and the community must be alert against them." According to the editorial page, then, Police Chief Parker had placed himself in the category of a fool or a conscious mischief-maker. I had always admired Parker's record and I felt that if anyone was a fool, it must be the blind man in the editorial department who refused to face reality and was living in an illusion, calling everybody a fool who didn't share that illusion.

The article went on to state:

> Patrolman James M. Johnson, 26, who was struck on the head by a gallon thermos jug wielded by one of the rioters, underwent X-ray examinations at Central Receiving Hospital to determine the extent of his injuries. Police Chief Parker said his department had been aware of a potential problem in Griffith Park for some time and disclosed as a result of conferences with the Parks and Recreation Department a month ago that ten men had been assigned to patrol the area near the concession Tuesday.
>
> "Everyone we know who was involved in the assault on the officers in the park was a Negro," Parker declared.
>
> . . . Eyewitnesses said the disturbance started when attendants at the merry-go-round ordered a group of Negro youths to leave the amusement vehicle after they refused to pay fares.
>
> Officers took one youth into custody but were almost immediately surrounded by 200 boys and men who attacked with bottles, rocks, baseball bats, and sticks.

The problem in Los Angeles had finally exploded before the public. I wondered how Mr. Towers was reacting to it, if he would agree with Pollyanna from the editorial page of the *Times* that a mere "incident," a "thing," had occurred in Griffith Park or that it was an actual race riot, as Police Chief Parker had branded it. Sometimes the obvious is the most difficult thing for people to see . . . often, because they don't want to see it.

22

A week before final grading, there was a faculty meeting. Mr. Towers gave a hearty public relations pitch. "Faculty, I'm very pleased to say that so far this year, I've had complaints about only one teacher's grading." His frozen smile didn't even turn in my direction. "That's batting a pretty good average, I'd say. Wouldn't you?"

The faculty applauded.

"Now in this last lap, let's not fall down on the job! Let's get the students over the hurdles and into the home stretch with flying colors! Remember, I'm not saying you shouldn't flunk anyone. Never have I said such a thing. I'm simply saying that we should do our utmost to help the students get good grades, recognizing their efforts, and realizing that all education is merely a preparation for life, and the necessary adjustment to the problems of life. When our students fail, we are, in effect, failing ourselves. So unless the student absolutely will not do a thing, and you have tried your very best to communicate with him, do not fail him!"

He then went on to speak about "the ethics of the profession," as he called it. "As teachers, as colleagues, it is important that we maintain the very highest code of ethics. We must stick together! After the Faculty Frolics this year, I received certain telephone calls which gave me the sad news that there was unprofessional dissension among us. I have also heard some comments made about our neighbor principal, Mr. Highsmith, and I consider these comments to border on slander. The fact remains that Mr. Highsmith has not been proven guilty of any crime. He was simply arrested for tearing down posters which advertised the suitability of a candidate for Superintendent of Public Education in California. As far as I can see, that is Mr. Highsmith's right as a voter. And the attorneys for the Board have seen that he has been released. He is back on his job as principal. Until such time as our superiors have judged his actions and allocated the charges where they see fit, we must disclaim any and all minor judgments of our own."

He then spoke about a vital bond issue in the coming election. It would mean bigger and better buildings for education. An example of the passing of a similar bond issue was our quarter million dollar auditorium in which such splendid programs as our Faculty Frolics had been performed—*and don't forget the Christmas program in which the name of Jesus Christ was not mentioned,* I thought, *or the Memorial Day program which failed to mention the name of one war dead.*

"Each of you teachers will be assigned a location which you will work for so many hours," he was saying. "You will hand out literature approving this issue—"

Anger exploded inside me. I had assumed a lot of roles as a teacher. I had been a glorified baby-sitter, a referee, a social director, an unarmed guard—but one thing I was not going to be was a puppet in the hands of politicians! Let them stand on their own street corners and hand out their own literature!

I started to speak my thoughts but held myself in check. Where the administration was concerned, there was still another role the teacher was supposed to assume—that of a monkey. "Hear no evil, see no evil, speak no evil."

When I went out to my car in the parking lot, I was surprised to find Mr. Zoel, the Negro custodian, waiting for me. He was a kindly man with a bright mind and, during the year, his advice had helped me out in a few rough spots. "Well, it's all over but the shouting, eh, Mr. Brent?" he smiled.

I grinned. "The shouting when they get their report cards, is that what you mean?"

He laughed gently. "You know, Mr. Brent, I've been working around schools for a lot of years now. I've seen 'em come and go, good and bad. I've learned to take teachers and kids all with a grain of aspirin, you might say."

I nodded. "I've taken a few grains of aspirin myself this year, Mr. Zoel."

"You've done real well," he said soberly. "I've watched you, Mr. Brent, and you shine out above most of the teachers we get. You've got the real interests of the kids at heart, and the interests of the Negroes, too."

"Well, thank you," I smiled. "I've tried but I'm not too sure whether I've succeeded."

"Trying is the important thing," he nodded wisely, "and it's because you've tried that Mr. Jesse Reese wants to meet you."

"Who is he?" I asked curiously.

"He's the local representative for the National Association for the Advancement of Colored People. He asked me to speak to you today and see if you'd be kind enough to come around to his house this evening. He'd like very much to talk to you."

"I'd be happy to, Mr. Zoel," I said. "It should be interesting to meet him."

He gave me Mr. Reese's address and after dinner that evening, I drove to his house. It was in a modest but pleasant section of the city. I tapped on the door and a nice-looking Negro woman answered.

"Come right in, Mr. Brent," she said cordially. "I'm Mrs. Reese. Mr. Zoel telephoned and we were expecting you."

I went inside an attractively furnished living room. "Please sit down. My husband is helping our older boy with his math but he'll be with you in just a moment."

She offered me coffee and had just moved out of the room when a fine looking Negro man came in. He extended his hand in a pleasant greeting. "So very happy you could drop in, Mr. Brent. I've heard some very good things about you."

"Thank you."

There was a knock at the door. Mr. Reese opened it and a short, chubby woman came in, enthusiastically smiling. She was white. We were introduced. She was Mrs. Mabel Holly, a former teacher in the Los Angeles school system. I wondered if her visit were coincidental or if she had come purposefully to meet me, too. Then I wondered why I wondered. Had I reached a point where I was suspicious of people with no reason? And what was I suspicious of?

But an uneasy feeling remained with me as Mrs. Reese served coffee and Mrs. Holly spoke, her broad smile with its trace of condescension reminding me so much of Towers. "How do you like teaching in a majority Negro school, Mr. Brent?" she asked.

"Speak right up and say what you think," Mr. Reese encouraged. "We want to hear it."

"Well . . . it has been rough," I commented hesitantly.

"Negro schools are rougher than white schools," Mrs. Holly agreed firmly.

"Exactly what do you mean by 'rough'?" Mister Reese frowned.

I answered, "For one thing, I feel that discipline is weak in the school where I teach."

"Do you blame Mr. Towers for that?" Mrs. Holly asked, thrusting her head forward in a birdlike gesture.

"I'm not blaming anyone," I said. "The situation itself is bad. The kids we have come from culturally deprived backgrounds. They are given a battery of I.Q.

tests and placed in groups according to their scores. If they have scored low, then not much is expected of them. Their potential is not taken into consideration."

"Then you disagree with the validity of the I.Q. tests?" Mrs. Holly asked, and the way she literally threw the question at me made me suspect she was probably a spy for the Board of Education who wanted to get proof that I was a "rabble-rouser," a "witch-hunter," and a promoter of "unprofessional dissension."

"I think we should consider the tests but not take them as final word for the child's potential ability," I said. "Children should be challenged, always, to improve on any previous record. Their imaginations should be stimulated—"

"And this hasn't been done in your school?" Mrs. Holly interrupted sharply.

I found my anger rising. "I tried this on what is supposed to be my lowest mental level group. Their improvement in just one effort was remarkable. However, I was told by my principal to give it up. He said that I should bring the work problems down to the children's previous levels."

"Then you would say the desired standard in your school is low?" Mr. Reese asked.

"Frankly, Mr. Reese, I don't think there is any standard," I said heatedly. "These kids are being sloughed off like stepchildren! And I believe firmly that unless the standards in black and white schools are the same, there can never be an equality of educational opportunity!"

"How can you be so sure the standards aren't the same in white schools as in black?" Mrs. Holly demanded.

"I did two semesters in white schools during my practice teaching year," I answered. "And even though it was only practice work, the difference between the children I dealt with then and the children I deal with now, and the difference in what is expected of them is—"

"The difference between black and white?" Mr. Reese asked, an ironic smile playing over his face.

"Yes!"

He nodded. "Mr. Brent, you are obviously a zealous man. Why don't you join us in our fight for equal education? Write up your experiences from the past year and your opinions and submit it to me. I'll present it to national headquarters. It will help in our crusade—"

"I am not a crusader, Mr. Reese," I interrupted. "I'm a teacher."

"What do you think of de facto segregation, Mr. Brent?" Mrs. Holly asked.

"I think that many people have warped the meaning of the Supreme Court decision," I replied. "They would take the Negro students out of the schools they would normally attend, in their own neighborhoods, and force them to go to white schools in far, unfamiliar sections of the city. This is frustrating for the children and I think it is a cruel method of trying to force race mixture."

"We must fight discrimination, Mr. Brent," Reese said quietly.

"You people say you think discrimination is inherently wrong," I said, "but you are constantly using it yourselves. How can you possibly justify this way of thinking?"

"I might appear that way on the surface but look at it from another angle. Years of discrimination have unfortunately placed the Negro ten yards behind his white contemporaries. And even if fairness reigned from now on, the Negro would still be ten yards behind. Something has to be done so we can catch up, Mr. Brent. Something has to be done to rectify the wrongs of the past."

"Mr. Reese, you are now talking about vengeance. You are making flat statements about the Negro problem. As I said, I am a teacher. I deal with children. You would use these children as social pawns to achieve what you feel would be fair to yourselves as a group. You would use the school as a weapon to achieve your goal. But let me tell you something. It isn't right for anyone to use children as a means to gain their own social ambitions. Our children should go to school for one reason only—to get an education!"

Mrs. Holly laughed nervously. "I'm sure there are many aspects to this problem you have never considered, Mr. Brent."

I rose. "Yes, I'm sure they are, Mrs. Holly," I said, and excused myself and left.

I was puzzled and upset by the meeting. What had been the purpose of it? What had they hoped to accomplish? And why *me?* What had I done to make Mr. Reese think I would want to join his crusade? I just wanted to teach! I wanted to be left alone and given the simple opportunity to do the best I could to educate young people! It didn't seem too much to ask and yet it was an uphill climb all the way.

When I got home, I glanced at a small, double-sheeted newspaper which was published monthly to keep teachers informed about what was going on in their world.

On the front page, there was a picture of a teacher supervising a playground. The caption beneath read HOW TO GET ULCERS. It said, "There she stands, a frantic figure with a ham sandwich in one hand and a whistle in the other." I went on to read the column below:

> Thus did Assemblyman Charles E. Chapel of Inglewood picture the typical California teacher a few years back as he argued eloquently for a bill designed to free the teacher from yard duty long enough to eat a quiet lunch, free from the ulcer-forming clamor of the playground.
>
> Today, thanks to CTA-sponsored (California Teachers Association) legislative action, that picture is pretty much a thing of the past. . . . The law placed in the hands of the State Board of Education responsibility for adopting rules and regulations fixing the duration and time of day of the duty-free lunch period and prescribing the conditions under which it would be allowed. The State Board subsequently adopted a rule calling for a teacher's lunch period of at least half of the regularly established noon hour, provided that in no event shall it be less than twenty minutes.

I read the last sentence again. It didn't make sense. Either they gave you thirty minutes or they didn't give you thirty minutes. Personally, I hadn't had more than fifteen minutes for lunch since I'd begun teaching. I read on:

> Is lunch duty-free? Are duty-free lunch period regulations being complied with in your district? If not, CTA's field service . . . should be notified. Methods

which may be needed to achieve compliance are under study.

It was very clear, I thought. They couldn't really do anything if we never got any lunch period at all! But they were "studying" methods. I could starve to death while they were studying!

All the ham sandwiches I'd bolted during the year seemed to repeat on me as I looked at another article in the paper: NOT ONE FILE PER TEACHER BUT FOUR. It stated that there were four distinct files kept on each teacher. A Service Folder, which was not secret, an In-Service Training Folder, which was not secret, an Employee Relations Folder (previously called the Confidential Folder), which was completely secret, and the Examination Folder, which was stated as being "mostly secret."

It said that any teacher could, at any time, examine the non-secret files to determine their standing on such items as "name change requests, oath of allegiance, evidence of age and citizenship, college transcripts, and their application for employment with L.A. city schools."

The teacher would not be allowed to see, however, "such trivia as debt complaints, derogatory correspondence from inside and outside the District, discipline reports, loyalty reports, references from inside District for exams (tracers), termination reports, etc."

All these facts were given at a meeting of Local 1021's Executive Board by a man named Roger Kuhn. It did not say who Roger Kuhn was. However, it went on to state that even though Mr. Kuhn "felt guilty about doing so, he was still carrying on the debate with Personnel Division" regarding the secret files. *Why should he feel guilty?* I wondered. Did he fear becoming a secret file himself? "The devastating arguments of that Division in defense of the secret tracers in particular boil down to this: that while open Performance Reports rate the teacher's past performance, the secret tracers, made prior to every exam, attempt to predict a teacher's performance as a contract employee."

So they've even gone into fortunetelling, I thought wryly. But the fact implied by the article was simple. A teacher would be foolish to complain about anything at all because he, and the complaint, would probably wind up in the "secret file." If something as vital to the education of our youth as total respect for the flag found no backing from the Board, they would certainly give no worry to the ulcer I felt forming or the ulcers of innumerable other teachers.

23

The last days exploded one into another. As I drove to school on the final morning, I felt like a runner must feel making the last plunge in the fifty-yard dash. But it would soon be over . . . the year that had begun with a fight and ended with—what?

I found that the school was surrounded with police cars, one on each corner. A walkie-talkie station wagon was in the middle of the block. One of the teachers was walking back and forth in the yard, peering through binoculars. It hardly represented the picture of a school as the school is represented, I'm sure, in the public mind.

Towers was in the yard. "What's all this for?" I asked him.

"Just taking precautions," he said weightily. "The last day is always the hardest."

The first day is always the hardest and the last day is always the hardest, I thought as I went on into school, and every day in between is pretty hard, too.

Roger Gates ran down the hall toward me. "I heard Billy Parrish is gonna get even with you today, Teach! This is Vengeance Day, you know!"

"Vengeance Day?"

"Sure! All the studs get even on the last day! Last year, they threw the old V.P. up in the air and he nearly broke his damn back!" He laughed heartily.

I went into the front office and signed in. "Do you want the Tuna Fish Casserole or the Meat Loaf?" Mr. Towers' secretary asked, referring to the special luncheon held for the teachers following dismissal.

"Tuna Fish," I said.

"One dollar and twenty-five cents," she nodded, "and we must have the money now."

I took the money from my wallet and gave it to her. As I waited for the change, I couldn't help thinking that payment in advance was probably the only guarantee there would be any luncheon at all.

Even on the last day, George Washington was waiting for me at the homeroom door. He followed me inside. "You gonna be here next year, Teach?" he asked hopefully.

"I don't know, George."

"Man, I sure hope so!"

"Thank you, George," I smiled. "Thanks a lot."

The bell rang. The homeroom boys came in as usual. George stood by the door, poised like an animal ready to leap. After the flag salute, when we were all seated, a couple of boys in the back of the room brought out a pair of dice and began throwing.

"Put them dice away!" George ordered. One of the boys threw the dice out the window. "And all you studs sit up straight! We're gonna give Mr. Brent a big all-round clap for what he's done for us and I don't want to hear nobody say nothin'!"

Obediently, the boys clapped.

All classes were speeded up so we could have a noon dismissal. Each class was more unruly than ever before but the Special class topped all previous performances. They outdid even themselves in a final display of industrious misbehavior during which Marion Blackwell came to me with an appeal for my safety. "Mr. Brent," she said softly, "I hear say the Chains are gonna take care of you like they're gonna take care of a couple other people 'round here. So I'd be awful careful when I leave school . . . if you know what I mean!"

The hands of the clock finally pointed to twelve—the end of the school year. Looking back, as so often happens, time had flown by. And I hadn't begun to understand what made my children tick. I didn't want them to go, suddenly. I wanted to hold on to them for just one more minute. If I could only find the right words . . . if I could manage to reach them just once. . . .

The loud-speaker system crackled and the Boys' Vice-Principal's voice came into the room. "Students, it is the end of another fine school year. Now it is time for you to relax, play and enjoy yourselves."

A whoop roared through the rooms and echoed down

the halls. I looked outside and saw the policemen stare tensely at the building.

The voice continued. "We want you to leave in an orderly manner, and as a warning to any members of any gangs we want you to know that police prowl cars are waiting for you on every corner of the school yard. So let's not anybody start anything. You will leave by grade as we call you over the public address system. You will not return to the school for any reason unless you have a note from the Principal or your teacher. We'll see you next year. Have a good summer and we look forward to next fall for another productive happy school year!"

As the children moved out, some of them calling their good-byes, I gathered together my papers and books. Finally, there was one student left in the room. It was Captain Smith. He stood in front of my desk.

"Well, so long, Captain," I smiled. "Have fun this summer."

His eyes were wide and uncertain. "Mr. Brent, is it okay with you—I mean, would you mind much if I—I took the Yellow Pages?"

With all my heart, I wished again for that one more moment. But I didn't have it. "Of course, Captain," I said. "You may take the Yellow Pages."

He grinned in relief. "Gee, thanks, Mr. Brent!" He got the directory and hurried out of the room.

In less than a moment, I heard an angry yelp from the hall, followed by shrill laughter. I ran quickly outside and found the Captain and Ruby Burns carrying on a tug-of-war over the Yellow Pages.

"Now you gimme these Yellow Pages, Radiation," the boy cried, "they're mine!"

"You simple-minded fink," Ruby laughed. "What you want 'em for? You can't even read 'em!"

I pulled the children apart and took the directory. "Now stop this!" I ordered.

Laughing wildly, Ruby dashed down the hall. Captain Smith just stood there, quietly crying.

"Come on, now, Captain," I said soothingly, "you're a big boy. Why do you want to cry over the Yellow Pages? They give them away free from the telephone company. You probably have one at home."

He looked at me tensely for a moment, controlling his tears, then he took the pages from me and carefully began thumbing through them, as if searching for something of momentous importance. At last, he found a series of pages which he rolled proudly in front of me. There were pencil marks on them, a strange, meaningless scribbling.

"You see, Mr. Brent?" he barely whispered.

"What is it, Captain?"

"Why, they're my ten-minute writings," he said proudly. "You didn't know I could write so good, did you?"

With this, he turned, and hugging his precious Yellow Pages to his breast, ran happily down the hall.

I went back into the classroom where I had been born as a teacher. I looked thoughtfully about. Had I died as a teacher there, too? The bulletin boards looked fine, just fine . . . all my pictures were hung evenly . . . and there wasn't a single thumbtack to distract.

I sat at my desk. I heard distant children's voices and the hollow echo of running feet. The empty room seemed suddenly crowded, as images repeated their role on the stage of my memory . . . Captain Smith crawling across the floor . . . a mass of scars on a girl's face—a girl they called Radiation—pulling those scars into a twisted smile as she goosed the crawling Captain . . . Angelina, in her low-cut peasant blouse, screaming defiantly, "Fuck you!" . . . Age-old fires of hate burning brightly in Marion Blackwell's eyes—fires that would never go out—as she hissed, "We Muslims are gonna' teach the white man one thing for damn sure—to *never say nigger!*"

Behind all the swiftly fleeting images was the enormously magnified face of Mr. Towers, looking on with smiling, Buddha-like calm.

In red, Billy raged, "I'll kill you, do you hear me? I'll kill you!"

In green, Towers smiled, "Send him to Social Adjustment. Have him write five hundred times—'It is wrong to kill'."

Red rage, green calm, white and black hate seethed all around me. I saw Griffith Park's merry-go-round, with an angry mob of Negroes throwing bottles, brickbats, rocks . . . Three hundred thousand Negroes ready to mob, rob, steal or kill to get what they wanted . . . *"Kill the white devils!"*

As if a giant death-ray gun had flared on target, the bright modernistic structure of my idealistic views disintegrated before my eyes. I might just as well wad my former views of the Negro problem up into an inadequate ball and throw them in the wastebasket. I might as well write on the blackboard five hundred times, *I give up*. In the blinding whiteness of naked truth, I felt sick to my stomach. As if from a distant echo chamber, I heard my sister say, "A Negro school? A ninety per cent Negro school? . . . Go to the Board and tell them you've changed your mind. Tell them you want to teach in a school near where you live. Tell them anything—but don't let yourself be thrown into a hotbed of blacks!"

I let myself be thrown into it, and it had been a hot hell . . . a tight little hell of my own personal construction . . . a hell built upon a beautiful dream . . . a dream built upon an earnest desire . . . a desire built upon a generous wish . . . a wish that all men were truly created equal by a loving and just God. Hadn't I the right to view God as just? Or was I actually trying to superimpose on God my own view of a just creation? And that was a right I didn't have, did I?

Lincoln had said, ". . . and dedicated to the proposition that all men are created equal . . . we are met on that great battlefield testing whether that nation or any nation so conceived and so dedicated can long endure . . ."

My mind focused sharply on the familiar words. ". . . *testing* whether that nation or any nation so conceived and so dedicated can long endure . . ." Lincoln hadn't said that anything was proven. He had merely said that the idea of equality was an experiment. And now, the whole concept of equality was on trial for all the world to be jury.

I recalled the letter President Lincoln wrote from Washington on August 23, 1863, to Horace Greeley. In the letter, he made his stand clear, didn't he? ". . . As to the policy I seem to be pursuing, as you say, I have not meant to leave anyone in doubt.

"I would save the Union. I would save it the shortest

way under the Constitution. The sooner the National authority can be restored, the nearer the Union will be 'the Union as it was.' If there be those who would not save the Union unless at the same time save slavery, I do not agree with them. If there be those who would not save the Union unless at the same time destroy slavery, I do not agree with them. My paramount object in this struggle is to save the Union, and is neither to save or destroy slavery. If I could save the Union without freeing one slave, I would do it; and if I could do it by freeing some and leaving others alone, I would also do that. What I do about slavery and the colored race, I do because I believe it helps to save the Union; and what I forebear, I forebear because I do not believe it would help to save the Union."

How we had twisted Lincoln's own stated motivation for the Civil War! And the challenge he put forth in the Gettysburg Address: "It is for us the living, rather to be dedicated here to the unfinished work which they who fought here have thus so nobly advanced. It is rather for us to be here dedicated to the great task remaining before us—that from these honored dead we take increased devotion to that cause for which they gave their last full measure of devotion. . . ." How crudely we had conceived of that challenge!

What had America given to its people? I thought. Inventions, industrialization, economics, freedom. . . . In all these, we had truly won the world's championship. Which of the four did we—did the world—consider above all? The first three were materialistic achievements. They meant a higher standard of living—a chicken in every pot, two cars in every garage, two freakish faces of television in every home. If we valued these above all, we'd be falling into the trap of the enemy's puny philosophy which measured greatness with materialism instead of eternal truths for men to live by.

But freedom—wasn't this the glittering jewel America could proudly put on display for the world to see, not in a diadem adorning the head of a royal monarch but in the hearts and minds of every American man, woman and child? Freedom—the majority dictating their will in a democratic society.

I saw America projected in miniature in my school. I wondered if the nation, if it were ninety per cent Negro, could "long endure." I wondered if the "test of endurance" would in the end prove the proposition Lincoln had challenged us to experiment with to be false, wishful thinking. I wondered if the "self-evident" truth in the Declaration of Independence, that all men are created equal, might not be proven the lie with which a naive nation had illusioned itself. Would the dream of equality prove the Achilles heel of America? Would there be only a funeral service for that great dream, and perhaps this great country, at the end of the "Freedom Road"?

I drove such depressing thoughts to the back of my mind, and hastily gathering my things, skipped the Tuna Fish Casserole and left the school for the very last time. I went downtown to the Board of Education which had left word they wanted to see me—to conduct my own funeral service as a teacher, I imagined.

This is the explosive yet compassionate account of what a young idealistic white man faced during his two years as teacher in two majority Negro schools in Los Angeles. His frustrations with school officials as well as with his students are clearly defined in a shocking picture of incessant violence and the seemingly indifferent attitude of school officials.

Here is the true story (with names changed) of incorrigible and intellectually sub-standard youngsters and also of others who against odds are striving for help, understanding, and an education, but who are afraid to give their best or to voice their true feelings because of reverse prejudice among themselves.

To summarize his point of view, we quote Mr. Kendall: "I do want to make sure that I say nothing that anyone hunting for excuses to obscure the truth as presented in my book can use. I want to avoid any possibility of being labeled 'pro' or 'con.' I want also to avoid the titles 'racist' or 'extremist.' God knows I'm simply deeply concerned over a serious social problem; no more no less . . . I sincerely hope my experiences will be of value in illuminating and solving the problem. . . ."

This is a book which some of Mr. Kendall's more fainthearted colleagues advised him not to write because the truth was too shocking. The majority of teachers urged him to tell this story because "it is desperately needed and should have been written long ago." This is one book that is impossible to put down, once started.